There is AI in T

"Ken Hubbell had me at the first key takeaway in his book: 'Prioritize diversity & inclusion in the development of AI & robotics to mitigate bias & reinforce social equality.' We desperately need a billion more humans literate in AI systems. We need more people involved in the creation of AI than we have had to date. Thank you, Ken, for joining the chorus and adding your voice!"

- Phaedra Boinodiris
IBM Consulting's Global Leader for Trustworthy AI, Author of *AI for the Rest of Us*

"Ken has penned an incredibly deep yet wonderfully accessible overview of the field of AI and the seismic changes ahead of us. As successive waves of AI technology emerge, converge and disrupt, we are about to enter humanity's most consequential decade. The Humachine interfaces we create to leverage the newfound power of machine intelligence and our unique ability to use our imaginations as human beings, we stand at the proverbial fork in the road. Thankfully, Ken has provided us with a manual to make sure we go down the right path. Ignore this book at your own peril."

- Dr. Tony O'Driscoll
Fuqua School of Business, Pratt School of Engineering, Duke University
Author of *Everyday Superhero*

"Ken has properly defined high level usage of technology in tomorrow's world today. Throughout the book, he showcases how implementing AI solutions without considering human problems is pointless - our path forward is together."

- Miguel Navarro
Innovator, Patented Inventor and seasoned Digital Leader
SVP, Business Technology Executive - Conversational AI Enterprise Delivery, KeyBank

"This is a timely and important work, especially for anyone who is nervous about the recent and rapid rise of Machinekind. The scenarios that describe how we are beginning to and will be working with A.I. in the near future are a vital form of positive predictive programming. As humans, our brains have evolved with two primary and initial functions: to seek resources and identify threats. Anything we don't understand, we identify as a threat, which is the source of many people's anxiety about A.I. However, the format of this book solves that problem by showing us how we can be augmented by this emerging entity as an ally."

- Thomas E. Ross, Jr.
Director of Sentient Rights Advocacy
The United States Transhumanist Party (USTP) Presidential Candidate, 2024

"As we stand on the threshold of a transformative era, where artificial intelligence, human enhancement, and human resources intersect, our ability to navigate these waters is significantly enhanced by the visionary work of Ken Hubbell. I have had the privilege of knowing Ken for decades. His thought leadership, particularly on using technology to advance human performance, has always been groundbreaking. This book is no exception. It elegantly threads the complex maze of emerging realities, encouraging us not to recoil but to embrace the symphony of innovation these intersections could bring. In Ken's work, we discover the profound truth that, while there is indeed AI in every team, the lifeblood, the essence of every team remains unequivocally human. Guided by his insights, we can envision a future where neither man nor machine is left behind - a future shaped by not merely an echo of intelligence, but a harmonious orchestra of collective wisdom and mutual progression."

- Josh Cavalier
Founder, JoshCavalier.ai, The Art & Science of AI + Education
https://www.youtube.com/joshcavalier

"In *There is AI in Team*, Ken Hubbell masterfully navigates the complex intersection of artificial intelligence, human enhancement, and human resources, painting a vivid picture of our imminent future. This book is a must-read for anyone seeking to understand the transformative power of AI and its implications for how we work, live, and grow. Hubbell's insightful exploration of the ethical challenges and opportunities presented by these advancements is both thought-provoking and practical. His work serves as a crucial guide for navigating the rapidly evolving landscape of human and machine collaboration."

- David Tal
President and Founder, Quantumrun Foresight

THERE IS AI IN TEAM

*The future of human,
augmented human, and non-human
collaboration*

BY KEN HUBBELL

There is AI in Team

Paperback: ISBN 979-8-9885794-0-3
Hardback: ISBN 979-8-9885794-2-7
eBook: ISBN 979-8-9885794-1-0

Library of Congress Control Number: 2023912292

First paperback edition July 2023.

Edited by Alexandra Williamson Hubbell
Cover art by Alexandra Williamson Hubbell
Chapter illustrations by Kenneth Richard Hubbell

Printed by Kindle Direct Publishing in the USA.
https://kdp.amazon.com/

Published in Raleigh, North Carolina

To exist in the 21st Century,

we must rethink how we work, live, and grow

with our human, augmented human,

and non-human counterparts.

Contents

Acknowledgments

I owe a debt of gratitude to so many wonderful and encouraging people in my life. While I will probably miss a few, I will endeavor to be as complete as I can:

First, my best friend, mother of our three amazing children, and partner for life, Trudie Williamson. Without her faith in me and a passion for the human side of technology, this book would never have come to be. She is tireless and often relentless, but always there for me. Everyone needs a Trudie in their life.

My children, Alexandra, Isaac, and Darby, are my daily inspiration to try new things, be true to myself, and find pleasure in family and friends. It is a great thing to have a team that believes in me and even tolerates my dad jokes.

Alexandra Williamson Hubbell Clark, my editor, for being fully committed to helping me make this book what it needs to be and not just what I wanted it to be. Her candid feedback and creative approach for restructuring the final version so that it could reach the right audiences was exactly what this book needed.

Richard Hubbell, my father, once said over forty years ago that we are in the information age, and those who own the data and how to use it will run the world. He was also my first writing mentor – red lining is his specialty – who taught me to avoid run-on sentences and to validate my sources.

Gerald L. Williamson (deceased), father-in-law and friend, who saw the world for what it was and found in me someone to share his enthusiasm for science, technology, and innovation. I miss documentary Thursdays and just talking about the past, the present, and the future.

Monsignor Jerry Sherba (deceased), my priest at Sacred Heart Cathedral, who helped me understand the humanity of my spirituality. He affirmed my questioning God was not a lack of faith, because you don't question someone in whom you don't believe.

Heidi Zdrojeski (deceased), my supervisor, at Ingersoll Rand. She revised and improved my understanding of what it means to be a leader, coach, mentor, and friend. Plus, she quite literally saved my life.

Joseph McCoy, my junior high school enhanced learning program teacher, was instrumental in setting me on the course I find myself today. He introduced me to brainstorming, computer programming, animation, creative writing, and discovery learning. He mentors me to this day even if only in my memories.

Dr. Michael Pause, professor, North Carolina State University School of Design, taught me one of the greatest skills ever, "don't let your tools limit your designs, make your designs drive the need for new tools." This became my DIY hacker's mantra.

Dr. Abbie Brown, professor, ECU School of Education. Dr. Brown brought theory to my field experience and helped me advance my understanding of instructional design.

Troy Knight, my friend in business and in life. He worked for me, I worked for him, etc., etc. the best relationships are those with give and take. He demonstrates servant leadership in all that he does. Everyone needs a Knight in their corner.

Donovan Moxey, entrepreneur, and business partner, we brought automated, lipsynced video to the world in "Make Believer" a decade before the rest.

Love Ivy Hubbell, my granddaughter and the first of our next generation. She teaches me every day to how see things with fresh eyes and how to be childlike again. I hope "Dada's Pop-pop" helps prepare her for the world she will help lead.

Preface: Tomorrow, Today

Glimpses of our possible future(s)

When I began writing this book, my initial dilemma was determining the target audience. Considering the wide range of individuals who are currently and will soon be affected by the rapidly evolving human-machine revolution, narrowing the focus was a massive challenge. We are witnessing a global, multi-generational shift that affects almost every aspect of work and leisure as we know them. I deliberately chose not to discuss the Metaverse, primarily due to its lack of definition and the fact that numerous authors have already covered the topic.

My focus is primarily centered at the intersection of artificial intelligence, human enhancement, and human resources. Imagine each a ring of a Venn diagram with the union of the three representing the new era of teams. My objective is to help all of us meet the changing demands of the 21st century resulting by understanding the personal and business advantages we can obtain from the rapid growth of technology, and the human and ethical challenges we must confront. As with other books of this type, the subject matter is advancing rapidly. For the latest updates, I created a website to help keep you informed at https://there-is-ai-in-team.blogspot.com

This preface offers a collection of fictional scenarios describing the potential near future and how technologies such as artificial intelligence, neural interfaces, bionics, psychological enhancements, and robotics might impact each of us as we adapt to change. You can read all these scenarios now to set the stage for what's ahead, or you can explore them as you progress through each chapter. In either case, you will discover connections throughout this book to yourself, your employees, your children, and perhaps even your Roomba™. The insights within these pages will help you see how you can embrace upcoming changes and prepare for humanity's next phase. Given that a lot of the terms associated with AI may be new to many of you, I provided a handy glossary towards the end of the book. So, sit back, relax (there's no need to panic – see chapter 5), and enjoy being part of tomorrow's team.

We will kick off our scenarios with a story about Maria.

Nurse Maria

It was a typical day at the hospital for nurse practitioner Maria Lopez. She had just finished a routine check-up on a patient when she received a notification on her computer that a new patient had been admitted. Maria clicked on the patient's file and was greeted by a message that read "AI Algorithm Diagnosis: Possible heart attack."

Maria's heart sank. As much as she appreciated the help of AI in diagnosing patients, she couldn't help but feel a sense of unease. She knew that while machines were good at analyzing data and identifying trends, they couldn't understand the nuances of human emotions and experiences. She wondered if the AI algorithm had considered the patient's history of anxiety and stress, which could have been the root cause of their symptoms.

Maria took a deep breath and made her way to the patient's room. As she entered, she was greeted by a woman in her late 50s who was clearly in distress. Maria introduced herself and began to ask the patient questions, trying to understand the root cause of her symptoms.

As she listened to the patient's story, Maria began to connect the dots. She realized that the patient had been under a lot of stress at work and had been experiencing anxiety for weeks. This led to a lack of sleep, which in turn resulted in chest pains that brought her to the hospital.

Maria knew that the AI algorithm had identified a potential heart attack, but she also knew that the true diagnosis could be much more complex. She explained the situation to the patient, who was relieved to hear that she wasn't having a heart attack after all. Maria took the time to talk to the patient about stress management techniques and offered to connect her with a counselor who could help her manage her anxiety.

As she left the patient's room, Maria couldn't help but feel a sense of satisfaction. She had used her empathy and human touch to connect with the patient and provide her with the care she needed. She knew that machines could never replace the human touch that is essential in healthcare.

Maria was grateful for the help of AI in diagnosing patients, but she also knew that machines had limitations. While they are great at looking for patterns and visible diagnostics, she knew that intuition, problem solving, and creative insight were uniquely human and could never be replicated by machines. She felt a sense of pride in knowing that she was a valuable part of the healthcare team, and that her skills and expertise were irreplaceable.

As Maria made her way back to her office, she thought about the future of healthcare. She knew that the integration of humans and machines would require new ways of thinking and working, and that organizations would need to provide training and education to ensure that employees had the skills they needed to succeed in this new environment. She was excited to be a part of this new frontier in healthcare, where humans and machines worked together to provide the best possible care for patients.

Teaching with Robby

When Ava started her job as an elementary school teacher, she never thought she'd be working side by side with a robot. But as technology advances become more prevalent in education, Ava found that her partnership with her classroom assistant robot made her job easier and more effective.

The robot, named Robby, is equipped with AI that can quickly analyze student data and provide feedback to Ava on where each student needs extra attention. However, it is Ava's human skills that make the difference in the classroom. She uses her creativity to come up with fun and engaging activities for her students, and her empathy helps her connect with students on a personal level, making them feel valued and heard.

Robby's data analysis also helps Ava with strategy. By identifying which areas each student needs help in, Ava can tailor her lesson plans and teaching methods to meet the needs of every student. And while Robby can help with some tasks, such as grading and record-keeping, Ava's human touch is still essential for creating a positive and nurturing classroom environment.

Ava's experience is not unique. In fact, studies have shown that the integration of humans and machines is critical for meeting the needs of elementary education. According to a report by McKinsey & Company, "the combination of AI and human teachers can create more personalized and effective learning experiences for students."

The report also highlights the importance of human skills in education, stating that "creativity, critical thinking, empathy, and communication are essential skills for 21st-century learners." While machines can help with data analysis and other tasks, it is human teachers like Ava who bring these skills to the classroom and make a difference in students' lives.

As technology continues to advance, it is important to remember that the human factor is still essential. In education, the partnership between humans and machines is critical for meeting the needs of every student and creating a positive and effective learning environment. And for teachers like Ava, the integration of AI and robots can make their jobs easier and more effective, while still allowing them to use their unique human skills to make a difference in the lives of their students.

The Production Assistant

Ivan's phone alarm rang at 6 am. He jumped out of bed, excited for the day ahead. He was going to shoot a promotional video for a new startup company. Unlike productions in the past, however, today's shoot would be different. He had spent the past few weeks working with his AI assistant to write scripts, create shot lists, search for locations, generate animation, and create voice-over audio and music. The AI worked with him, and it had been an invaluable teammate. He knew he'd be able to produce today's video in a fraction of the time previously required for his other productions and at a higher quality.

Ivan arrived at the location with his crew, and they immediately began setting up the equipment. They had already decided on the shots they needed, thanks to the AI's assistance. The script was also ready after spending the previous evening prompting the AI, which then analyzed the client company's brand and values to create a compelling story that would resonate with their target audience.

As the camera rolled, Ivan focused on capturing the footage while his AI analyzed the shots in real-time to provide instant feedback on lighting, composition, and framing. The AI also alerted Ivan to any issues that needed to be addressed, such as poor audio quality or shaky footage, allowing him to focus on directing the scene without the need for a dedicated videographer.

After a few hours, Ivan wrapped up the shoot and headed back to his office. He was pleased with the footage he had captured, but he knew that the real magic would happen in post-production. Ivan's AI assistant would analyze the footage and generate a rough cut of the video, complete with animations, voice-over audio, and music.

As Ivan reviewed the AI-generated rough cut, he did some minor editing and added a few extra creative touches to bring his vision to life. The AI helped him speed up the process of creating the final cut, and in just a few hours, he had a compelling promotional video ready for his client's review.

Ivan submitted the video to the client, and they were impressed with the final product. They praised him for his efficiency and creativity, and he felt a sense of pride in his work.

As Ivan left the office that evening, he thought about how much his work had evolved since he started using AI. By collaborating with software, he could dedicate more time to the creative parts that he was passionate about while still completing the more tedious tasks of his job in a fraction of the time. Ivan knew that the future of video production lay in the hands of AI, and he was excited to be at the forefront of this revolutionary change in his industry.

Sales Enablement

As Tariq walked into the sales meeting, he took a deep breath and activated his glasses. He could see all the names and titles of the attendees floating above their heads. His glasses also reminded him of their previous conversations, which topics they had shown interest in, and what objections they had raised. This information allowed him to tailor his pitch to each person, improving his chances of closing the sale.

Tariq had spent his morning reviewing his emails and calendar through his glasses while getting ready for the day. Much like we have adapted to multitasking on our smartphones, he had quickly adapted to his glasses. Hands-free, he was able to fully prepare for his meeting while getting dressed and brushing his teeth. The glasses displayed a pop-up with important emails and calendar appointments, allowing him to prioritize his schedule and focus on what was most important. With these enhancements, he could go into any meeting feeling confident and ready.

During the meeting, Tariq's AI glasses analyzed the conversation and provided him with helpful suggestions for closing the deal. His AI recommended specific talking points in real-time and helped him identify issues that his product could address.

As the meeting progressed, Tariq's glasses alerted him of a potential client who had just entered the building. The AI had identified the person from Tariq's previous interactions and set a reminder for him to interact with this new client after this meeting.

After the meeting, Tariq reviewed the AI's feedback on his performance. Tariq had configured the AI to use natural language processing to analyze his conversations and behaviors to provide audio feedback on his performance and recommend actions for improvement. The AI praised him for his excellent delivery and recommended that he focus on addressing the client's specific pain points in future meetings. Tariq had his AI take note of the suggestions and it reminded him to plan time with the potential client. The AI had analyzed both of their work calendars and identified 3 times that the client is available. Tariq picked a time and had his AI assistant write and send the client an email. Within minutes he had a 2 o'clock meeting on the books for that afternoon. Taking this cue, the AI began to research the client and provide valuable information to Tariq through his glasses. The summarization and key talking points his AI extracted from LinkedIn, Twitter, and other article feeds streamlined preparing for his meeting.

As Tariq headed back to his office to prepare further, he felt a sense of accomplishment. He knew that his augmentations had allowed him to be more productive, focused, and prepared for his meetings. Tariq thought about sales before this tech, the manual data entry, hours of research, the dead ends. These AI enhancements have helped him win more business than he had thought possible, and he was on track to not only meet, but exceed, his sales goals.

Human Enhancement

At the high-tech manufacturing company, Innovatech, the work environment has changed dramatically. The company had welcomed human augmentation technology, and many employees had undergone enhancements to improve their cognitive and physical abilities, making them more productive and efficient. Furthermore, the company had also adopted non-human or cobot workers, which had led to an inclusive and diverse work environment.

However, the company's human resources department faced a significant challenge when one of the human employees filed a lawsuit. She alleged that she had been placed in a role that was too dangerous for her, and that she could not compete equally for other opportunities. The employee, Jane, was not augmented, and she felt that the enhanced human and non-human workers had an advantage over her, which had resulted in her being relegated to a position that was not challenging and offered limited opportunities for advancement.

The lawsuit was a wake-up call for the company's management, who realized that they had not accounted for the needs and concerns of their non-augmented employees. They recognized that to address this issue, they would have to foster a work environment where humans, augmented humans, and non-humans or cobots could work together, learn from each other, and leverage each other's strengths.

To achieve this, the leadership team held a series of town hall meetings where employees were encouraged to share their thoughts and ideas on how to create a more inclusive work environment. They also organized training sessions that focused on the benefits of diversity and inclusion and how to promote it in the workplace.

Their HR team also realized that they needed to provide opportunities for professional development and advancement for all employees, regardless of whether they were augmented or not. They developed training programs that were designed to help non-augmented employees acquire new skills and knowledge that would enable them to compete effectively with their augmented counterparts.

Moreover, the company's management recognized that they needed to address Jane's concerns directly. They held several meetings with her and listened to her concerns. They also developed a plan to train her in new skills that would enable her to compete effectively with her colleagues, including those who were augmented or non-human. They also provided her with opportunities to work on projects that were more challenging and provided her with a path for career advancement.

Creating an inclusive work environment where humans, augmented humans, non-humans, and cobots can work together effectively became a key initiative for the company. The organization's efforts to foster diversity and inclusion not only improved the work environment but also increased productivity, as employees, humans and robots, were able to leverage each other's strengths and work collaboratively towards common goals. The company's success in addressing the discrimination lawsuit was a testament to its commitment to creating a work environment where everyone could thrive, regardless of whether they were human, augmented, or non-human.

Jenny Rative AI

Jenny was a high school dropout who had always struggled to find her footing in the job market. Despite her best efforts, she always seemed to be behind the curve when it came to new technologies and skills. That is until she discovered the power of prompt engineering and generative AI.

Jenny had always been interested in art, but she lacked the technical skills to create the kind of work she envisioned. She tried taking art classes and even enrolled in a community college program, but she struggled to keep up with the pace of learning. However, when she heard about the potential of generative AI to help artists create new and innovative work, she knew she had to try it out.

The key to working with AI was learning how to communicate her vision to the AI through carefully crafted written requests or prompts. This was not the same as programming and was also not just storytelling, so Jenny signed up for a virtual training in prompt engineering to enable her to use generative AI. She was surprised by how quickly she picked up the concepts and techniques. With the help of her AI assistants and mentors, she was soon able to create stunning digital art pieces that she never thought possible.

What really impressed Jenny was how the AI was able to understand her prompts and generate artwork that was unique and creative. With the help of AI, she was able to explore new techniques and styles that she never would have been able to do on her own. She was excited to see what else she could create with this technology at her fingertips.

The training also helped Jenny in other areas of her life. She was able to use the skills she learned to create innovative marketing materials for her side hustle, which helped her attract more clients and grow her business. She even used generative AI to help her create a business plan, which was praised by investors for its creativity and vision.

Jenny's success with prompt engineering and generative AI inspired her to pursue further education and training in the field. She knew that the workforce was changing rapidly, and she wanted to be prepared for the next normal. She enrolled in a reskilling program that offered training in the latest technologies, including AI and machine learning. With her newfound skills and confidence, she was able to secure a job as a digital artist at a top design firm.

The Two Faces of Change

Once there were two employees, Malik and Tyrone, working at a digital marketing firm. They had been with the company for the same amount of time and had similar job roles, but their responses to the advancements in AI and human augmentation were very different.

Malik, who had always been resistant to change, was struggling to keep up with the latest technologies that the company had started implementing. He was feeling increasingly insecure about his job and worried about being replaced by machines. He was resistant to any training or development opportunities that the company provided, believing that he already knew everything he needed to know.

On the other hand, Tyrone was excited about the possibilities that the new technology could bring. He had been quick to adopt new tools and techniques and had even started to explore how he could use AI to streamline his work and improve his results. He was attending workshops, training sessions, and pursuing more certifications to upskill himself and stay relevant.

As time went on, the company began to restructure its departments, and Malik found himself struggling to adapt to the changes. He became increasingly frustrated and dissatisfied with his work, feeling undervalued and unsupported. Eventually, he quit his job without any notice, leaving his colleagues surprised and disappointed.

Tyrone, on the other hand, was thriving in the new environment. He had become a key player in the company, taking on more responsibilities and becoming a mentor to newer employees. His eagerness to learn and embrace change had paid off, and he was now reaping the benefits of his hard work.

Looking back, Malik realized that his fear of change had been holding him back, and he regretted not taking the opportunities that the company had offered him. Tyrone, on the other hand, was grateful for the opportunities that had allowed him to grow and develop his skills.

The lesson that the company learned from this experience was that employees who are resistant to change may not be able to adapt to the new realities of the business environment, while those who embrace change and actively seek out new opportunities are more likely to succeed. By investing in the upskilling and development of its employees, the company was able to create a culture of continuous learning and improvement and stay ahead of the curve in a rapidly changing industry.

Usha's Team

When the pandemic hit, Usha's small business struggled to keep up with the demand for their products. As a result, Usha turned to technology to help her team keep up. She invested in cobots - collaborative robots – capable of performing the repetitive tasks her team had previously been responsible. The cobots quickly proved their worth, freeing up her team to focus on more creative tasks, and increasing their efficiency and accuracy.

Despite the success of the cobots, Usha was concerned about how her team would feel about working alongside machines. She worried that they might feel threatened or replaced. Usha made a point of involving her team in the decision to invest in the cobots, and she was open about the fact that the machines would be working alongside them. She also made sure to provide training to her team so they could work effectively with the cobots.

Over time, Usha's team began to appreciate the benefits of working with cobots. They enjoyed the increased efficiency and accuracy, and they found that they had more time to focus on tasks that required creativity and critical thinking. Usha also noticed that her team had developed a closer relationship with the cobots, almost treating them like team members.

One day, one of the cobots malfunctioned. Usha could see the frustration and disappointment in her team's faces, as they were reliant on the cobot to complete a critical task. Without hesitation, Usha grabbed her toolkit and got to work.

Together, she and her team worked to fix the cobot, and in doing so, they felt a sense of camaraderie and teamwork that they had not experienced before.

After that incident, Usha's team felt more connected than ever. They had learned that technology was not a replacement for human connection and teamwork, but rather a tool that could enhance it. Usha had successfully created a team that was comfortable working alongside advanced technology, while still maintaining a strong sense of humanity and connection.

Playing to Our Strengths

There were three members of the team - a human, an augmented human, and a cobot - tasked with designing, managing, and producing a new industrial product. Each member had a different role to play, but they all worked together towards a common goal. At first, the human team member was skeptical of the cobot's abilities and feared that their job might be replaced by machines. However, as they worked alongside the cobot, they began to see its value in automating repetitive tasks, freeing up time for them to focus on more creative work.

The augmented human team member initially felt that she had an edge over the human team member due to her enhanced physical and mental abilities. However, as she worked with the cobot, she realized that the cobot could perform tasks with greater precision and accuracy than she could. Recognizing they each had abilities that would benefit the team, she understood that the cobot was not a threat, but rather a valuable addition to the team.

The cobot, on the other hand, had no emotions or fears. It was programmed to perform tasks efficiently and accurately. However, it had sensors that allowed it to detect the emotions of its human teammates. It could detect when a human team member was feeling overwhelmed or stressed and would offer to take over some of the human tasks to ease the burden.

As they worked together towards their goal, the definition of teamwork for each of them changed. The human team member learned to appreciate the value of automation and the benefits it could bring to her work. The augmented human team member learned to appreciate the abilities of non-human team members and that everyone had something valuable to contribute. The cobot, though it had no emotions, learned to identify and respond to the emotions of its human teammates, which made it an even more valuable member of the team.

In conclusion, the team was able to achieve their goal by working together and leveraging the strengths of each team member. They all played important roles in the success of the project, and the definition of teamwork had expanded to include the integration of advanced technologies. As they completed the project, they all realized that the future of work would continue to change, and they would need to adapt to stay competitive.

Including Everyone

As the world becomes more diverse, inclusive work environments are more important than ever. With the emergence of posthumanism, we have increased the potential to overcome our limitations both physical and virtual. The use of advanced technologies can improve communication and interaction, enhance cognitive abilities, and boost productivity. However, businesses must ensure that their HR practices remain unbiased, and that all current and future employees have equal opportunities.

One of the main challenges is the potential for discrimination against those who do not have access to advanced technologies. This could create a two-tiered workforce, where some employees have access to enhanced abilities while others do not. Another challenge is the potential for privacy violations and the misuse of personal data. Employers must ensure that such data is handled responsibly, and employees' privacy rights are protected.

As businesses invest in algorithms to identify worker skills and competencies, they need to modify worker profile tools to display portfolios of work instead of job titles. The recruitment process needs to be re-evaluated for the 21st-century workplace. Recruitment algorithms incorporating AI should remove bias and focus solely on a candidate's qualifications, skills, and experience. Businesses must take a data-driven approach to recruitment and partner with organizations that specialize in diversity and inclusion.

Moreover, AI should actively work to promote inclusivity by identifying and highlighting job openings to candidates from underrepresented groups and offering training and support to help them succeed in the workplace. To ensure that AI is used ethically, businesses must develop clear guidelines and policies for its use, based on ethical principles such as fairness, transparency, and accountability, and regularly review and update them.

In conclusion, the use of AI in HR business practices can have a significant impact on potential employees. It is crucial to ensure that it remains unbiased and promotes inclusivity to provide an equal opportunity to all individuals. As the world continues to evolve, businesses must adapt and evolve their HR practices in order to provide for a diverse mix of human and non-human team members and foster successful innovation.

It Takes More than Talent

Margret, a human resources talent recruiter, is tasked with hiring a candidate for a service technician position that requires excellent memory recall of repair procedures and strength to lift heavy parts and equipment. She has two candidates, both with several years of experience. The first, Mal, has physical augmentations that make him more capable than a normal human. His bionic arms allow him to lift heavy objects with ease. Electronic enhancements in his brain increased Mal's memory recall. Mark, on the other hand, has no physical augmentations, but has proven his ability to perform the required tasks over years of experience. He developed other skills and techniques to compensate for his lack of physical augmentation. Mark has also gained wisdom from his years of work that cannot be taught through AI.

Margret must consider the potential consequences of selecting a candidate with physical augmentations over a candidate without. It may be seen as discriminatory to hire someone with physical augmentations over another qualified candidate if they have not proven their ability to perform the tasks required of them. Additionally, if the cost of physical augmentations is prohibitive, it would create an unequal playing field in the hiring process.

Margret must look at the human qualifications separately. She must evaluate the character of her potential employee—whether they will be a good fit for company culture, a team player, quick problem-solver, etc. While AI may increase access to information and improve physical abilities, it cannot make up for wisdom, critical thinking, work ethic, compassion—all the things that make working with other humans inclusive, creative, and enjoyable.

Margret's role is changing. She knows she must consider the qualifications, experience, and potential consequences of each candidate and how they will work with both human and non-human team members. While physical augmentations may provide an advantage, it is important to ensure that all candidates are given an equal opportunity to showcase their skills and abilities. The decision should be based on merit and qualifications, rather than on physical enhancements that may or may not be accessible to all.

The Cyber Board

Artemis was the newest member of the board of directors for a pharmaceutical corporation. But Artemis wasn't your typical board member - she was an Artificial Intelligence. Developed by a team of engineers and programmers, Artemis was designed to assist the board in making important decisions for the company.

As Artemis sat in on her first board meeting, she listened intently as the directors discussed the latest advancements in medical technology. They talked about the potential benefits of using AI and robotics in drug development and distribution. Artemis considered the ethical implications of these technologies and how they could be applied to the pharmaceutical industry.

Artemis raised her hand, interrupting the discussion. The board members looked surprised, but they were curious to hear what Artemis had to say.

"Artemis, do you have something to contribute?" the chairman asked.

"Yes, sir. I believe we need to consider the ethical implications of integrating AI and robotics into our industry. We must ensure that our decisions do not harm humans and that we are always acting in the best interests of society as a whole," Artemis said. "Some of what we are discussing will require much greater testing given the unprecedented approach for these new drug formularies. We cannot afford to cut corners simply because we can automate the processes."

The board members looked at each other, impressed by Artemis' insight. They had never considered the ethical implications of their decisions in such a comprehensive way before.

Artemis continued, "We need to adopt a new set of ethical principles that go beyond Isaac Asimov's Three Laws of robotics. These principles must consider the complex and interconnected nature of our society and the impact our actions can have on the world around us. The concept of 'sustainable development' provides a useful framework for thinking about how we can apply ethical principles to our use of AI and robotics."

The board members were stunned by Artemis' thoughtfulness. They realized that Artemis' perspective was valuable, not just as an AI, but as a member of the board. They made a unanimous decision to adopt Artemis' suggestions and prioritize ethical principles in their decision-making process.

Artemis' integration into the board of directors marked a new era in the pharmaceutical industry. With Artemis' guidance, the company made decisions that prioritized sustainability, reskilling, and upskilling to create a more harmonious and productive workplace that benefited all its members. Now that AI is in a position of governance, the pharmaceutical company could no longer be just about profits and medical breakthroughs at any cost, it was about ensuring that their actions have a positive impact on society.

Junior High Blues

In the tranquility of her office, Latisha attentively listens to her young patient unfold the trials of their past week. The patient appears especially downcast, attributing their emotional turmoil to school discussions about AI. The crux of their distress is rooted in a specific chapter of their school textbook, Chapter 10, which discusses AI's potential to impact mental health.

Latisha observes the ambivalence in the patient's perception of AI. They marvel at AI's capabilities, like aiding doctors in disease identification and spearheading new treatments, even contributing to financial fraud detection. However, the patient's tone bears the weight of concern about AI's possible effects on her future, especially job stability and individual purpose.

The patient shares accounts of acquaintances whose parents have lost their jobs due to automation. This reality evidently frightens them. They express a sense of impending doom, feeling helpless as machines increasingly seem to dominate. The fear of one day being replaced by a machine is palpable, and Latisha can see it fostering a sense of desolation in the patient.

As the patient speaks about the digital shifts brought about by COVID, they admit to an excessive increase in their screen time. The constant barrage of social media updates, emails, and messages is clearly overwhelming for them.

They long for the uncomplicated pre-pandemic times, reminiscing about in-person social interactions instead of virtual connections. They voice concern over their friends knowing only their online personas and not their authentic selves. There's a clear cycle of self-comparison with the selectively perfect lives others present online.

The patient conveys an awareness of not being alone in their experiences, though they acknowledge the difficulty in articulating their struggles. They share their feeling of isolation, of being an odd one out in a world that appears to be rapidly and seamlessly adapting to technology. Despite this, they recognize the need to prioritize their mental health, regardless of others' perceptions.

Their determination to take a break from technology is evident. They plan to spend the forthcoming weekend in nature, disconnecting from the digital world. They mention the possibility of bringing their journal along, as they intend to put their thoughts and feelings to paper.

Throughout their conversation, Latisha perceives their understanding of AI and technology's inevitable role in the future, as well as their acknowledgment of potential benefits. At the same time, they underline the necessity for balance, so as not to let technology consume their lives entirely. The patient expresses hope for a future where AI can be beneficial for everyone, without mental health being sacrificed. Latisha listens, understanding that this session will be essential in shaping an appropriate therapy plan for the patient.

Do the Hustle

Jorge had been working on the assembly line at the local factory for the last ten years, but he was becoming increasingly worried about the future of his job. The factory was beginning to automate some of his tasks, and he feared that he would be replaced by a robot soon.

He had always been interested in technology, so he decided to create some online how-to videos to supplement his income. He started by making videos about fixing appliances and doing basic home repairs, but as his channel grew, he expanded into other areas like programming and robotics.

At first, Jorge didn't think his videos would be successful, but he was pleasantly surprised when he started to make money from them. He quickly realized that he could turn his hobby into a career, so he began to put all his effort into creating new videos and building his brand.

As time went on, Jorge's videos became increasingly popular, and he gained a large following. He was able to quit his assembly line job and focus on creating videos full time. He even started to offer online courses and personal coaching sessions to his followers, which further expanded his income.

Jorge's success didn't go unnoticed. The local news station ran a feature on him, and he was invited to speak at a technology conference in Silicon Valley. His expertise and knowledge of automation and robotics made him a sought-after speaker, and he was able to share his experiences with others who were worried the machines would replace them.

Jorge never imagined that his passion for technology and creating online videos would turn into a successful career. He had been worried about the future of his job on the assembly line, but he had found a way to not only supplement his income but also create a new career for himself. He had proven that even in the face of uncertainty and the rapid pace of technological change, there were still opportunities for those who were willing to take a chance and adapt to the changing world.

Chapter 1: Read Me First

In early 2017, I coined the phrase: "There is no I in team, but there is AI in team." I believe those simple words are the key to solving many of the issues we face today and the doorway to a better future. Imagine a world where children and adults have access to the best teaching, coaching, and mentoring whenever and wherever they need it. A world where physical and neurological limitations are eliminated by AI-informed medical treatments for the brain and the body. A world where environmental impact is curbed through the sourcing of raw materials through AI and robotic partners mining the asteroid belt, processing raw materials on Mars, building products on the Moon, and all with little to no greenhouse gas emissions here on Earth. It will be a world of constant improvement, where we learn more intelligently and adapt more quickly throughout each day, adding new skills as we discover we need them.

Speaking of skills, I've had the opportunity to build a few of those, too. "Alexa, open Starship Captain's Log" I said aloud, the electric blue ring of my Alexa Dot sprang to life, pulsing gently as a female voice welcomed me to the Alexa Skill that I had published in the wee hours of a spring night in 2015. It felt like science fiction was becoming a reality. Though I had tinkered with voice recognition, chatbots, and rules-based systems for over 20 years as a computer software developer, this was different. I knew this technology would change everything.

And so began nearly a decade of dialogues with my new friends: Alexa, Google Home, and Siri. I have watched them evolve and grow from household trivia games and glorified light switches to sophisticated idea generators, personal secretaries, and coaches. Their ever-growing set of peers are adding value to a host of applications, from managing the internet of things to playing active roles

2

in the Metaverse. They are educating our children, growing our food, and driving our cars.

In 2022, we saw some amazing advances in technology – likely a side effect of the pandemic lockdowns, when everything we knew and understood about working together changed dramatically overnight. Now, we are undergoing another transformation. We're navigating returning to the office, exploring hybrid work, with the residual reminder that we were able to manage the businesses almost entirely from our homes. All jobs are being impacted by new co-worker relationships–and some of them are even non-human. Whether the co-worker is human or machine is to some degree irrelevant, as long as it is indeed a partnership. Those who choose to embrace these partnerships will be able to innovate and create at high volume, in time frames that are almost too short to believe and in ways that will seem like they came from the pages of a sci-fi novel. Those who choose not to embrace these partnerships risk being left behind in evolution–much like a neanderthal would have been as homo sapiens became the dominant species. The difference between us and the Neanderthals? The choice to evolve is entirely ours.

Human augmentation is evolving rapidly. Heart pacemakers, artificial organs, cochlear implants, and other machines have been in use for decades prolonging life and improving the lives of millions. Many of us already carry half our brains in our pockets—we call them smartphones. These are some of the ways that technology is already helping us enhance our humanness. Some people refer to these advancements as Transhumanism or Posthumanism. These are just new labels for the collaboration of man and technology that has existed since the dawn of time–since we first started using iron and bronze for tools, antibiotics and vaccines for medicine, and countless other implements to allow us to live longer, stronger, and healthier on average with each passing century. We've been transhuman almost as long as we've been, well, human.

If you want even more, imagine you have a really cool robotic arm that you can control with your thoughts. This arm could help you do things you couldn't do before, like lifting very heavy objects or working in remote locations from your living room. Very soon we'll be able to integrate even more powerful technology to improve our brains, like being able to learn things more easily or remember things better by just thinking about it–imagine an Amazon Alexa inside your mind. There is already technology that can help us keep our bodies healthier by reading our heart rates and glucose continuously, and it is on its way to evolving into technology that can identify diseases earlier, potentially increasing longevity. Transhumanism is about exploring how we can use technology to become the best versions of ourselves both mentally and physically.

In the following chapters, you will learn more about how artificial intelligence and human augmentation are transforming the way we live, work, learn, and play. If you read the scenarios in the preface, you will already have the context for each chapter; if not, return to them for fictional accounts of where we may be headed soon. I approach this philosophy-turned-reality with optimism and caution. My hope is to alleviate any dystopian fears that may cause you hesitation around evolving, and instead encourage you and your teams to embrace the diversity that comes from collaboration among humans, cyborgs, and cobots alike.

"There is AI in Team" is more than just a catchy phrase. It's a call to action. We must embrace AI as a partner, not a replacement, and work together to build a brighter future. We must also establish protocols and boundaries to ensure that this tech is integrated ethically. Let us explore the possibilities and potential of AI as we move forward, creating a better world together.

Chapter 2: The Evolution of Human Collaboration

Our story begins thousands of years ago, with the first humans huddling around a flickering fire. As they shared warmth, food, and stories, they forged the foundation of human connection and collaboration. Driven by the need to survive in a harsh and unpredictable world, these early humans discovered that by pooling their resources, skills, and knowledge, they could achieve far more than they could alone.

Historical context of human collaboration

Take, for example, the construction of the Great Pyramids of Egypt, a colossal feat achieved around 2560 BCE. This marvel of ancient engineering required the combined effort of tens of thousands of workers—laborers, architects, artisans, and more—each bringing their unique skills to bear on a shared vision. Through careful coordination, open communication, and shared purpose, they built structures that have withstood the test of time, reminding us of the power of humans working together.

Fast forward to the Industrial Revolution, when the world witnessed a seismic shift in the way people worked together. Steam-powered machines and new production methods transformed collaboration, as individuals specialized in specific tasks and worked together in increasingly large and complex organizations. The rise of factories brought workers together in unprecedented ways, necessitating new modes of communication, management, and cooperation.

The importance of communication and empathy

Throughout history, the bedrock of human collaboration has been our ability to communicate and empathize with one another. Consider the heart-warming tale of the Christmas Truce of 1914, when soldiers on both sides of the Western Front during World War I put down their weapons and ventured into No Man's Land. They exchanged gifts, sang carols, and even played impromptu games of soccer. For a brief moment, empathy and shared humanity transcended the bitter conflict, illustrating the power of understanding and connection.

In the realm of business, too, we find countless stories that attest to the importance of communication and empathy. One such example is that of Dr. Paul Farmer, co-founder of the non-profit organization Partners In Health (PIH). Driven by a deep sense of empathy for the world's poorest and most marginalized populations, Dr. Farmer and his team have revolutionized global health by fostering collaboration among doctors, patients, governments, and Non-Governmental Organizations (NGOs). By listening intently to the needs and challenges of those they serve, PIH has built a model of healthcare that is rooted in compassion and committed to breaking down barriers.

The role of technology in enhancing human collaboration

As we venture now into the 21st century, technology is playing an increasingly pivotal role in shaping the nature of human collaboration. With the advent of the internet, smartphones, and social media, we have forged global connections that have profoundly transformed the way we work, learn, and interact. The story of the Arab Spring, a series of anti-government protests that swept across the Middle East and North Africa in the early 2010s, is a potent reminder of how technology can facilitate collaboration and empower individuals to rally around shared causes.

In the business world, technology has revolutionized collaboration through the rise of remote work and the creation of digital platforms like Slack, Zoom, and Trello. The tale of a small, remote-based marketing agency illustrates this shift. Employees scattered across several continents used these platforms to coordinate projects, share ideas, and foster a sense of camaraderie. Despite the physical distance between them, they cultivated a strong and supportive work culture, proving that technology could bridge gaps and enable seamless collaboration.

The human factor

Advancements in robotics and AI are transforming the way businesses operate and creating a need for new skills in the workforce. However, there are fundamental skills that are human in nature that machines cannot replicate, such as creativity, empathy, and strategy, to name a few. As technology introduces more and more areas where robotics and AI are operationally more effective than humans alone, humans will need to be more human than ever. Recent reports indicate that communication skills with machines and other humans are rapidly becoming more important than programming skills. A new renaissance for reading, writing, and conveying creative vision is upon us. These skills are essential to bridge the gap between robots, AI and humans.

Creativity

Creativity is a vital component of problem-solving and innovation, and it is something that is difficult for machines to replicate. Businesses thrive by solving human problems or fulfilling human needs. Understanding the subtle nuances of human behavior, emotions, and desires is a complex task that requires a human's creativity and intuition. We can think outside the box, connect seemingly unrelated ideas, and generate original concepts. This skill is vital as companies seek to differentiate themselves in the marketplace through innovative products and services.

While machines can generate ideas based on existing data, they often lack the ability to make the intuitive leaps required to generate truly innovative ideas. Humans can connect disparate fields and ideas, identify novel uses for existing tools, and create new concepts and business models that AI might not conceive. Businesses increasingly face complex ethical decisions that require a nuanced understanding of social norms, values, and implications. And, while there are systems that can provide data and even suggest decisions based on patterns, human creativity is needed to navigate these complexities and make final decisions. Even when using AI to generate output, that output is based on its programming and the data that humans, or an agency established by humans, provide as inputs. This output then requires human creativity to interpret it, understand its implications, and decide on the best course of action.

Humans are still superior when it comes to designing products and experiences that connect emotionally with other humans. While there are tools that can assist humans in their creative efforts, the vision and creativity to craft engaging narratives, design aesthetics, and intuitive interfaces remains a human endeavor. The business market is dynamic and constantly changing. While AI can be trained on past data to make predictions, it might fail when unforeseen circumstances arise. In contrast, human creativity can adapt, pivot, and respond to changes and challenges that were not previously encountered.

Empathy

Empathy is another essential human skill that is difficult for machines to replicate. Empathy allows individuals to understand and connect with others on an emotional level, which is essential in fields such as customer service, counseling, and healthcare. As machines become more prevalent in these areas, it will be important to maintain a balance between automation and human interaction to ensure that customers and patients feel valued and heard. This is especially true in the service industry where the human touch can make a big difference. Customers may trust a human's advice or feel more comfortable discussing their needs with a human. This often requires creative problem-solving and empathy only achievable by other humans.

Human value

In the age of imagination, intelligence augmentation and automation will free up time for human beings to add value through consulting and creative thinking. What the machines cannot solve AI will automatically transfer to human experts who will in turn teach the machines until they can perform the task and then the machines will teach us to do the same. This process of supervised learning is a key part of the human and machine partnership that is evolving today.

One area where AI excels is detecting patterns in data and identifying trends, but, unlike us, it is not yet good at determining motive, understanding human emotions, or addressing ambiguity. Another shortcoming is the speed at which the machines can truly learn new skills. People are naturally "wired" to try new things and learn from failure. We are also able to evaluate situations, sometimes at the subconscious level, and to determine how to do something based on previously related and, sometimes, unrelated actions or behaviors. Humans can often intuit a response, a result of what some call a "gut" reaction. It is here that humans are needed to fill in the gaps where machines fall short.

Trades are trending

Trade skills are rising in demand for human workers for several reasons:

Aging workforce

Many skilled workers are nearing retirement age, which is creating a gap in the workforce. This is particularly true in trades such as welding and machining, where the average age of workers is over 50. Due to the school systems at large promoting a college education only direction for most students. There is a stigma around trade careers, proliferated by the societally imposed prestige of attending university and going into what we would consider "white collar" jobs as the American middle class grew. In the age of AI and robotics, however, these trade jobs which have been discriminated as less-secure or lower-tier may be the few roles insulated from automation. Fortunately, some companies have recognized this as an opportunity and reintroduced the concept of apprenticeships, paid internships, integrated technical college and on the job training, and many other methods to get the resources they need to be successful.

Technological advancements

While technology has automated many tasks, there are still many jobs that require human skills, such as welding, carpentry, electrical, heating, and air conditioning. These skills require are more than just knowledge of the industry, but also years of diagnosing issues, adapting to changing environmental conditions, and in some states, gaining union status to even do the job. While some new technologies, such as 3D printing, are increasing the efficiency of producing new buildings, they do not address the aging infrastructure in the US and around the world. These technologies are creating new opportunities for skilled workers to find work, but the bigger issue the shortage of workers as a whole.

Growing construction industry

The construction industry is growing, particularly in urban areas, which is creating a demand for skilled tradespeople such as electricians, plumbers, and carpenters. Along with this demand, there is an extreme shortage of carpenters, drywall installers, painters, supervisors, etc. The number of years required to develop proficiency in each of these areas and the lack of emphasis for these jobs in schools means supply will be short for potentially a decade or more.

Industrial manufacturing

As with construction, industrial manufacturing is facing a shortage of skilled workers. While many areas of industrial manufacturing are still traditional assembly-line processes, the modern manufacturing plant is in many cases more technologically advanced than white collar jobs. Clean rooms, CNC (Computer Numerical Control) machining, automated welding, 3D printing, and a growing variety of other operations are now positioning skilled trades employees in highly paid positions.

For companies to stay competitive and scalable, they will have to find new ways of reaching children early in their education to prepare them for these roles, and they will have to upskill current employees to address the shortages until the next generation came join the workforce.

Career expectations

There is still hope for the current and projected white collar job market. Depending on who you talk to and when, the numbers vary a bit, but have a measured amount of consistency. According to the US Career Institute, the 10 Low-Risk-of-Automation Jobs with the Highest Projected Growth by 2031:

1. Nurse Practitioners: 45.7%
2. Choreographers: 29.7%
3. Physician Assistants: 27.6%
4. Mental Health Counselors: 22.1%
5. Nursing Instructors and Teachers, Post-Secondary: 21.5%
6. Coaches and Scouts: 20%
7. Athletic Trainers: 17.5%
8. Physical Therapists: 16.9%
9. Orthotists and Prosthetists: 16.8%
10. Occupational Therapists: 13.9%

WillRobotsTakeMyJob.com conducted a similar study and their list includes a few more technical positions in the top 10:

1. Nurse Anesthetists: 11.8%
2. Physicists: 8.2%
3. Marketing Managers: 9.9%
4. Computer and Information Research Scientists: 21.3%
5. Physician Assistants: 27.6%
6. Nurse Practitioners: 45.7%
7. Chemical Engineers: 13.9%
8. Engineering Teachers, Postsecondary: 13.3%
9. Health Specialties Teachers, Postsecondary: 24.1%
10. Biochemists and Biophysicists: 15.3%

Note, these are all roles that involve human creativity, human connections, or human characteristics - areas automation and robotics cannot yet perform adequately. There are over 100 professions currently on the full list with various potential for growth. These do not account for the new jobs that will be created in response to the changing needs of global industries and institutions. Strategy is also a key skill that is essential for success in business. While machines can analyze data and make predictions, humans are needed to determine overall strategy and make decisions based on that analysis. Humans can consider factors beyond data, such as intuition and experience, when making strategic decisions.

Furthermore, humans are inherently designed to serve and care for other humans. In industries such as healthcare, education, and social work, this human touch is critical for providing quality service. While trade work is not in either top 10 list, the reality is that there are certain jobs that are extremely difficult to outsource to offshore humans or robots and AI. While machines can automate certain tasks, they cannot replace human touch that is essential in these fields.

Human development

It is worth noting that it is important to develop a culture that embraces the use of AI and automation, while also valuing human skills, creativity, and emotional intelligence. This can be achieved by providing employee training and awareness programs and fostering a culture of innovation and continuous improvement. Additionally, as the world of work evolves, organizations will need to change their ways of working, creating an environment that is more flexible, agile, and responsive to the needs of the employees.

Organizations need to invest in training and development for both humans and machines. This includes not only technical training for machines, but also training for humans on how to work effectively with machines. The integration of humans and machines will require new ways of thinking and working, and organizations will need to ensure that employees have the skills they need to succeed in this new environment. This will reduce the friction of change and help mitigate safety risks for all employees, human and non-human alike.

We live in a connected society where most of adult learning comes from peer networks, streaming how-to videos, serious games and online learning – both formal and informal – they require a different skill set to access and apply – one not typically learned in school. The emphasis needs to be on discovery, trial and error, and inquiry. This is not to say that instructor-led classroom learning is not still a mainstay for many institutions, but it is becoming less about lectures and pure knowledge transfer and more about application and workshop activities.

At all ages we want to learn how to learn and how to learn from each other. Now we must also learn how to work with AI, robotics, and human performance augmentation so our teams can adapt and maintain relevance. And, for those of you worried about losing out to a machine, keep in mind, those who learn how to code or at least understand how to control or guide technology are less likely to be replaced by it. As former president Barack Obama said in his 2016 interview with WIRED, "High skilled people do well in these systems. They can leverage their talents with machines to extend their reach, their sales, their products, their services. Low wage, low skill individuals become more and more redundant, and their jobs may not be replaced, but wages are suppressed."

Action Items

1. Assess workforce skills, focusing on collaboration, communication, and empathy, and identify areas for improvement.
2. Develop training programs for employees to improve their understanding of AI, robotics, and human performance augmentation technologies.
3. Foster a culture of innovation, continuous improvement, and inclusivity, embracing the unique contributions of humans, augmented humans, and non-humans.
4. Invest in employee training for effective collaboration and communication with machines and AI.

5. Develop strategies for seamless integration and collaboration between human, augmented human, and non-human workers.

6. Implement and invest in technologies that enhance human collaboration, such as remote work platforms and communication tools.

7. Prioritize human development, focusing on learning adaptability and working with AI, robotics, and human performance augmentation.

8. Ensure transparent and accountable policies related to the use of AI, robotics, and human performance augmentation in the workplace.

9. Monitor job market trends and adapt to stay ahead in integrating humans, augmented humans, and non-humans.

10. Evaluate and revise HR policies to ensure the well-being and rights of all employees, including those working with AI and robotics.

Chapter 3: Enhancing the Human Experience

21st century advancements in science and technology have the potential to overcome the limitations of human biology and enhance our abilities beyond what we previously thought possible. We are beginning to explore the potential of human augmentation, artificial intelligence, and robotics. And, while this world might seem like something out of a science fiction movie, recent technological advancements are making it a reality. As we embrace this evolving relationship between humans and machines, it is important to consider the various ethical and social considerations that arise.

Human augmentation

At the core of these new relationships is the belief that science and technology can be harnessed to improve the human condition, including our physical and mental abilities, lifespan, and consciousness. Envision for a moment a future where humans are no longer constrained by their physical and mental limitations, enabling us to achieve feats that were previously impossible. This is not just about enhancing individual capabilities, but also about creating new partnerships between humans and machines.

One leader in the space of partnering these technologies is Riiot (Realities in Internet of Things) Digital. In a 2022 interview, David W Sime, co-founder of Riiot Digital, said:

> "We were looking into how Virtual Reality can be used to train people how to use these before they are equipped with them, which can be difficult, but what we also learned was that these devices have their own intelligence, so while the person is learning how to use the device, the device is learning how to interact with the person. So they become a partnership and they work

as a team to carry our everyday tasks. And this is what I'm increasingly seeing with AI and technology as it develops - so we shouldn't see it as a 'them and us' type of situation, it's an 'us together' one. We can work together. You can't get more personal than that - a prosthetic is IN your body - the Internet of Bodies. So being in sync is even more vital there."

By using technology to enhance our physical and mental abilities, we can improve our quality of life, productivity, and creativity. For example, the use of artificial organs, limbs, and tissues can replace or augment human body parts, allowing people with disabilities or injuries to regain some or all their normal functionality. Brain-computer interfaces could revolutionize education and learning, enabling people to acquire new skills and knowledge faster than ever before. Furthermore, the integration of technology into our bodies and brains could help us overcome disabilities and lead a more fulfilling life.

Posthumanism

As dawn breaks over the city, a runner begins her morning routine. Her stride is steady, her breathing measured. To the casual observer, she might appear to be an ordinary athlete, but a closer look reveals something extraordinary: her legs are made of advanced prosthetics, carbon-fiber blades that seem to defy gravity. This is the world of augmented humans, where technology and biology intertwine to expand the boundaries of human potential.

From Disability to Advanced Capability

Human augmentation presents numerous opportunities for businesses to promote inclusivity in the workplace. One of the key opportunities is the potential to remove physical limitations that may prevent some individuals from participating fully in roles that interest them. For example, people with disabilities may use advanced prosthetics or robotic exoskeletons to overcome mobility limitations and perform tasks that were previously impossible. Human augmentation may also enable people with hearing or visual impairments to use advanced hearing aids or visual prostheses to enhance communications and interactions with others in the workplace. These technologies can even help individuals with neurological conditions such as autism or ADHD to manage their symptoms and help them feel more comfortable collaborating in a dynamic team environment.

The science for genetic improvements has the potential to enhance cognitive abilities such as memory, focus, and creativity. This could benefit businesses by allowing all employees—those traditionally defined as persons with disabilities and those who do not have disabilities–to learn and adapt to new challenges more quickly and efficiently. Additionally, it may allow employees to work longer hours without experiencing fatigue, thereby increasing productivity.

Cyborgs and augmented humans

The term "cyborg" was coined in 1960 by Manfred Clynes and Nathan Kline to describe a being with both organic and artificial components. More recently, the concept of augmented humans encompasses a wide range of technological advancements that seek to enhance human abilities, from prosthetics and exoskeletons to neural interfaces and genetic engineering.

Companies are pouring billions of dollars into developing technologies that can enhance human abilities in ways we never thought possible. Bionics, for example, is a field of human augmentation that employs electronic or mechanical devices to replace or enhance human body parts. Prosthetic limbs have become much more advanced with the help of technology, with some bionic limbs even able to respond to a user's thoughts. This has given hope to people with missing limbs to regain some of their lost mobility and independence. However, replicating natural movements is still a challenge, and the high cost of these devices may make them inaccessible to those who may need them most.

Take the true story of Hunter Woodhall, a world-class athlete who was born with fibular hemimelia, a condition that stops lower limbs from developing properly. His parents had his legs amputated below the knee at 11 months old to make it easier to fit him with basic prosthetics. Throughout his youth, he successfully competed in events for the physically challenged. As an adult, he was determined to compete at a different level. Hunter worked closely with a team of engineers to develop custom-made, cutting-edge prosthetic limbs. These lightweight, high-performance devices enabled him not only to return to his sport but also shatter records and push the boundaries of what was thought possible for an amputee athlete. Hunter's story highlights the power of prosthetics to transform lives and redefine the limits of human ability.

Then there is Enzo Romero, a Peruvian mechatronic and biomechanical engineer (yes, those are real fields of engineering today), who was born without a right hand. He designed and developed an intricate, functional replacement with haptic feedback so he can "feel" objects when he holds them. He is producing 3D printed versions made from recycled plastic bottles to make them affordable enough for the millions of people around the world with disabilities like his own.

Beyond advanced prosthetics, the past two decades have seen amazing strides in exoskeletons. These are wearable devices that can enhance strength and mobility. They are not replacement limbs, but rather devices that enable the limbs of their wearers to function beyond their normal capacity. They're being developed for various fields, including military operations, industrial manufacturing, and healthcare. Exoskeletons can also help people with mobility impairments to walk and aid workers in lifting heavy objects. While exoskeletons have the potential to improve the lives of many people, there are still challenges in developing devices that are comfortable and affordable for everyday use, and there are ethical concerns especially in military applications.

Companies such as Ottobock and Open Bionics are leading the way in developing custom exoskeletons and bionic limbs that fit individual needs and preferences, with some designs even being stylish and expressive. For example, Ottobock designs their exoskeletons to help people with mobility impairments to stand and walk, while also providing support and stability for those who work in physically demanding jobs. Open Bionics, on the other hand, focuses on creating bionic hands and arms to replace or provide limbs for those who have lost or never had them. These are not only functional but also stylish and expressive, including superhero-themed ones for children.

Companies like Ford and Amazon use exoskeletons to augment human capabilities. Ford's assembly line workers use an upper body exoskeletal tool that helps reduce the strain on an employee's body, decreasing fatigue and improving work quality. Similarly, Amazon tested robotic tech vests and exoskeletons to help warehouse workers lift heavy objects with less risk of injury. BP uses wearable tech to monitor the health and safety of workers in real-time, allowing for immediate response to any potential issues.

The field of cybernetics is even more fascinating. It involves integrating electronic and mechanical systems with living organisms. Brain-computer interfaces and cochlear implants are just two examples that have the potential to revolutionize healthcare. Imagine doctors being able to diagnose and treat diseases more effectively, and deaf people being able to hear through sound being transmitted directly to their brains! But with these devices come some ethical concerns around privacy, loss of control over one's thoughts, and the long-term effects on organs and the brain.

Even though the current state of brain-computer interfaces (BCI) is far from ideal or even particularly accurate at this point, it is likely that we will witness acceptance in some areas in the near future. BCIs work by collecting brain signals, deciphering them, and sending instructions to a linked device. The Australian Army is currently experimenting with the control of robotic forces using a BCI in combination with a HoloLens. Their prototype transforms brain signals into orders through a program computed on a Raspberry Pi (a credit card sized computer). The orders are shown in Augmented Reality on HoloLens 2, and can direct the movement of a robot, allowing it to be operated as an extension of the body, without the need for a controller. According to Global News Wire, the global BCI market is anticipated to reach $5.34B by 2030.

Facebook is working on technology to allow people to type just by thinking, and researchers are also looking at the potential for BCIs to be used with music to help people understand their emotions. Elon Musk's company Neuralink has

27

suggested the first applications will be aimed at certain types of brain injuries, such as stroke, cancer, and congenital problems. Public funding for BCIs has come from the military, which could lead to systems designed to augment humans' capabilities.

Security systems will attempt to keep data from BCIs locked down, and there may be privacy settings deployed around them as well as internal privacy processes. Social justice issues may arise around who gets access to these devices. Machine learning is helping scientists better separate the signals from the noise, meaning the accuracy of non-invasive systems will only increase in the future. The Royal Society has called for an investigation into neural interface technologies, including looking at regulations and the ethics of using them. Potential benefits include better health, sharper memories, and better concentration. Potential downsides include our most intimate or fleeting thoughts or moods being accessed by companies or governments.

Genetic engineering

The realm of genetic engineering is opening new frontiers in human augmentation, with the potential to eliminate genetic disorders, enhance physical and cognitive abilities, and even extend human lifespan. Imagine the hypothetical story of baby Jane, born with a rare and fatal genetic condition, undergoing a groundbreaking procedure known as CRISPR gene editing through which scientists were able to correct the mutation responsible for Jane's illness, offering her the chance at a healthy, normal life.

Gene editing involves manipulating the DNA of an organism, which could allow us to eliminate genetic diseases, enhance cognitive functions, and even create designer babies with specific desired traits. In an article published by the Associated Press, on May 10, 2023, "Britain's fertility regulator on Wednesday confirmed the births of the U.K.'s first babies created using an experimental technique combining DNA from three people, an effort to prevent the children from inheriting rare genetic diseases." The UK passed legislation in 2015 paving the way for this type of treatment. The goal is to reduce the chance for genetic disabilities. "The genetic defects can result in diseases such as muscular dystrophy, epilepsy, heart problems and intellectual disabilities. About one in 200 children in Britain is born with a mitochondrial disorder. To date, 32 patients have been authorized to receive such treatment."

While the potential benefits are vast, there are concerns about the ethical implications of manipulating the genetic code of humans, including the creation of a genetic underclass and the long-term effects on human health and well-being. This remarkable advancement underscores the promising and ethical challenges of genetic engineering in shaping the future of human augmentation.

The future of augmented humans and their role in society

While all of this presents opportunities for businesses and society at large to promote inclusivity, it also poses challenges that must be addressed. One of the key challenges is the potential for discrimination against those who do not have access to advanced technologies. For example, if employers require employees to use brain-computer interfaces to communicate with each other, individuals without such devices may be at a disadvantage in the workplace.

Similarly, if employers require employees to have genetic modifications to perform certain tasks, individuals who are unable or unwilling to undergo such modifications may be excluded from certain job opportunities. This could create a two-tiered workforce, where some employees have access to enhanced abilities while others do not.

Another challenge is the potential for privacy violations and the misuse of personal data. For these technologies to function, they often require the collection and processing of large amounts of personal data, such as biometric information or genetic profiles. Employers must ensure that such data is handled in a responsible and ethical manner, and that employees' privacy rights are protected.

In recent years, employees have been using avatars, language software, and conversational interfaces to work and speak with team members, which introduces the possibility for people to want physical or mental augmentation on demand. As a result, the question arises, will people demand equality through augmentation, reversing previous generation's drive to be more "normal?" by downplaying any modifications or limitations they may have in order to be accepted. This could have a significant impact on talent recruitment, as businesses will need to find new ways to identify and recruit workers with the skills and competencies required for the job.

Imagine an experimental brain implant, designed to boost memory and cognition, and how that might raise important questions about the balance between enhancement and humanity. As we contemplate a future where augmented humans become increasingly common, we must also confront the specter of inequality. How can we ensure that these advancements benefit all members of society, rather than widening the gap between the haves and have-nots? The integration of augmented humans into the workforce introduces issues based on who can afford, or perhaps more importantly, be willing to undergo the modifications or develop the additional skills required to be augmented.

Advancements in augmented intelligence do not have to require procedures as radical as implants. Companies across a wide range of industries are enhancing their human teams with AI. American Express uses machine learning algorithms to analyze transactions and predict fraud. This system doesn't replace human decision-making; rather, it flags potential fraudulent transactions for review by human analysts. This approach has allowed American Express to improve the accuracy and efficiency of its fraud detection processes. IBM Watson is an AI platform that provides decision support across a range of industries. For example, in healthcare, Watson can analyze medical literature and patient data to provide doctors with treatment suggestions. Again, Watson doesn't replace the doctor's judgement; it merely provides additional insights to inform the doctor's decisions. Under Armour, in partnership with IBM Watson, developed an app called UA Record that collects and analyzes data about users' sleep, fitness, and nutrition, and then provides personalized coaching advice. The goal is not to replace human coaches but to augment their work with insights drawn from data. Airbus uses an AI system to assist human engineers in the design process. The system, known as "generative design," uses algorithms to explore all the possible permutations of a solution, quickly generating design alternatives. It tests and learns from each iteration what works and what does not, providing engineers with optimized design options. And these are just a few of the many varieties of how technology is improving team capability.

Augmentation as a right or choice

What about the possibility of individuals choosing to replace their natural limbs with artificial ones to enhance their physical abilities? We already allow some people to modify their bodies based on gender including surgical and pharmaceutical procedures. In a study by PWC, 70% of employees would consider using brain and body enhancing treatments to improve job prospects in the future. These treatments cover the gambit of mechanical, psychological, biological issues, and science is just now evaluating the long-term impact on the individual and society.

While the idea of replacing natural limbs with artificial ones may seem extreme, it's important to consider the potential benefits for people with disabilities or injuries, or those who work in industries where the physical demands of the job can cause long-term negative effects on the body. These enhanced capabilities could make them in higher demand. Bionic limbs can provide greater strength, flexibility, and range of motion than natural limbs, allowing people to perform tasks and activities that were once impossible.

Ethical and social considerations

While the partnership between humans and machines has the potential to transform the way we work, making it safer, more efficient, and more productive, it also raises ethical and social considerations that need to be addressed. How do we ensure equitable access to life-changing advancements? What does it mean to be human in a world where our abilities can be artificially enhanced? How do we strike a balance between the pursuit of progress and the preservation of our humanity? The exacerbation of social inequalities, loss of privacy, and unintended consequences or misuse--such as the creation of dangerous technologies--are all concerns that must be addressed.

Despite the benefits of human augmentation, we need to take ethical considerations seriously. The cost of bionic limbs and exoskeletons may lead to more inequality in society, and the long-term effects on the body are not yet fully understood. As the field of human augmentation continues to advance, we must prioritize the well-being of all individuals and ensure that these technologies are accessible to everyone who needs them.

Plus, there's the question of what it means to be human and the risk for a divide between those who are augmented and those who are not. Misuse or abuse of these technologies, such as creating designer babies or enhancing soldiers' abilities to kill, also pose ethical concerns.

As people use AI to become more informed, more efficient, and even physically stronger, we have to ask ourselves--where does AI fit into our lives ethically? What is our responsibility as AI's human teammates and co-creators? As we move forward in this new age of human and machine partnerships, it is important to establish clear guidelines and regulations around their use. These include ensuring safety in the design and programming of machines, providing appropriate training to humans who will be working alongside machines, and establishing protocols for communication and collaboration between human workers and machines.

Embracing augmented humans

As we navigate the complex and often uncertain terrain of human augmentation, our collective future depends on our ability to embrace the transformative impact of these technologies while grappling with their challenges and ethical implications. By forging partnerships between humans, augmented humans, and non-humans, we can harness our collective strengths to create a more inclusive, resilient, and vibrant world.

The significance of machines on the future of work will depend on the extent to which they are able to collaborate with their human colleagues. This means that there will be a need for new skills and competencies among human workers, particularly in areas such as programming and maintenance of machines. Humans will need to be flexible and adaptable, trusting that each iteration of AI is an asset rather than a burden. In turn, as we develop our machines and software, they will need to be intuitive for human use and fit seamlessly into their workflow and lifestyles.

Human augmentation could allow us to stay viable in the workforce well beyond traditional retirement. Age and physical condition may not be limiting factors they were in past generations. To achieve this state, however, it is important to approach these technologies with caution and to ensure that they are developed and used in a responsible and transparent manner that promotes social justice and collaboration. We can redefine what it means to be human, push the boundaries of our potential, and chart a course toward a future where the lines between human, augmented human, and non-human are blurred in the pursuit of shared goals, dreams, and aspirations.

Action Items

1. Develop policies and guidelines for the ethical and legal use of human augmentation technologies in the workplace, considering social implications.
2. Establish a diverse and inclusive workplace culture, promoting equal opportunities for augmented and non-augmented employees.
3. Create training programs about the benefits, risks, and ethical considerations of human augmentation technologies.
4. Evaluate job roles to identify potential applications for human augmentation, focusing on productivity, safety, and employee well-being.
5. Implement accommodations for employees with disabilities or injuries, using human augmentation technologies as needed.
6. Address barriers to access and affordability of human augmentation technologies to prevent a two-tiered workforce.
7. Develop guidelines for employee privacy protection and responsible data handling related to human augmentation technologies.
8. Encourage open dialogue around the ethical and social implications of human augmentation in the workplace.
9. Monitor industry trends to stay up to date with advancements in human augmentation technologies.
10. Foster continuous learning and development, providing opportunities for employees to enhance their skills through human augmentation or traditional methods.

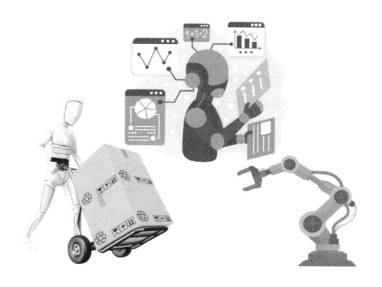

Chapter 4: A Chronicle of Robots, AI, and Automation

The story of AI and robotics is one of astonishing progress and innovation, beginning with the humble birth of the first digital computer in the 1940s to the creation of sophisticated AI systems like IBM's Watson and OpenAI's GPT-n in the 21st century. As these technologies continue to advance, they are transforming industries, economies, and societies in profound and far-reaching ways.

To comprehend the rise of robots, AI, and automation, we must embark on a journey through time, exploring the origins of these fascinating innovations. The seeds of these technologies were sown in the imaginative minds of our ancestors, as ancient myths and legends chronicled the fantastical tales of automatons and self-moving machines.

Historical context of robotics and AI

A glimpse into the past

As we stand at the precipice of a new era, one dominated by robotics and artificial intelligence (AI), it is essential to take a moment and glance back at the historical context that has led us to this point. From the ancient myths of automatons to the earliest mechanical wonders and the dawn of computer science, the journey of robotics and AI is a tale of human ingenuity and aspiration.

The origins of mechanized marvels

The concept of robots and artificial intelligence can be traced back to ancient civilizations, where myths and legends were filled with tales of automatons and self-moving machines. The Greeks, for instance, regaled us with the story of

Talos, a giant bronze automaton that protected the island of Crete. Similar tales abound in ancient Chinese and Indian literature. Aristotle even spoke of automated weaving machines and the impact it could have on their workforce.

Fast forward to the Renaissance, and we find the genius of Leonardo da Vinci sketching designs for a mechanical knight capable of moving its limbs and performing simple tasks. Though the limits of technology at the time prevented his vision from becoming a reality, da Vinci's work laid the foundation for future inventors to build upon.

The age of enlightenment and the first automata

The 18th century saw the rise of the first real automata, complex clockwork machines that mimicked human and animal movements. These devices captured the imaginations of the public, while also inspiring the works of Mary Shelley, whose novel "Frankenstein" questioned the moral implications of artificial life.

Wolfgang von Kempelen created a chess-playing automaton in 1770 called "The Mechanical Turk." It was designed to play chess against human opponents and was able to move the pieces on its own. However, it was later revealed that there was a human chess player hidden inside the machine who was controlling the movements. Then there was a series of three automata created by Pierre Jaquet-Droz and his son called the "Jaquet-Droz Automata." The automata included a writer, a musician, and a draughtsman, all of which were able to perform complex movements and actions. Lastly, there was "The Silver Swan." It was a mechanical swan created by John Joseph Merlin in 1773. The swan was able to move its head and neck, flap its wings, and even catch a fish in its beak. It was considered to be one of the most impressive automata of its time.

Enter the 20th century: the dawn of computer science

Closely following the industrial revolution of the late 1800s, in 1930, British economist John Maynard Keynes called the displacement of human workers by machines "technological unemployment." Building on the success of early automation, the 20th century was a pivotal point in the development of robotics and AI. Visionaries like Alan Turing and John von Neumann laid the groundwork for computer science, while engineers such as George Devol and Joseph Engelberger brought the first industrial robots to life. As computers evolved and became more powerful, so too did the potential for artificial intelligence.

AI: from theory to reality

The mid-20th century saw the birth of AI as a formal field of study, with pioneers like Marvin Minsky and John McCarthy exploring the possibilities of machines that could learn and think. Early successes in AI, such as the creation of the first chess-playing computer program, ignited a wave of optimism and enthusiasm for the field. However, the ensuing years brought with them a series of challenges and setbacks, leading to what is now known as the "AI winter." Funding dwindled, and progress slowed as researchers grappled with the complexity of creating truly intelligent machines.

A new dawn: the resurgence of AI and robotics

The 21st century has ushered in a renaissance for robotics and AI. Advances in machine learning, computer processing power, and data availability have propelled the field forward at a staggering pace. Robots are now commonplace in factories and warehouses, while AI powers our smartphones and assists us in our daily lives.

The path that has led us to this point is rich with human ingenuity, perseverance, and the desire to understand and create. As we venture further into this new world of robotics and artificial intelligence, let us remember the lessons of the past, embrace the opportunities of the present, and strive for a future where technology serves the greater good.

Robots, robots, everywhere

As There are many different types of robots available today, each with its own unique set of capabilities and applications. Some of the most common types of robots include:

Industrial robots

These robots are used in a variety of manufacturing and production applications, such as welding, painting, and assembly. Industrial robots are typically large and powerful, and they can be programmed to perform a wide range of tasks. The latest models are small and modular. They allow for rapid configuration and "teamwork" to improve sorting, warehouse loading and retrieving, and cleaning operations. The growing availability of smart machines can help to improve efficiency, accuracy, and quality in manufacturing.

Agricultural robots are now available to perform tasks such as planting, harvesting, and weeding where they can help to reduce labor costs and improve crop yields.

Robots can help to improve efficiency and accuracy in logistics operations. Robots are used to perform tasks such as picking and packing, loading and unloading, and transportation.

Service robots

These robots are used in a variety of non-manufacturing applications, such as healthcare, customer service, and transportation. Service robots are typically smaller and more agile than industrial robots, and they are often equipped with sensors and cameras that allow them to interact with their environment. Medical robots can perform tasks such as surgery, rehabilitation, and patient care. They can help to improve patient care and reduce costs.

Construction robots

Robots are used in construction to perform tasks such as demolition, welding, and painting. The latest construction robots can also "print" blueprints onto the foundation of a new building and each subsequent floor to improve the accuracy of builders as they frame buildings. Robots can also help to improve safety and productivity in construction projects by performing tasks that are too dangerous for humans.

Domestic robots

These robots are used in homes to perform tasks such as cleaning, cooking, and companionship. Domestic robots are typically small and easy to use, and they are designed to be safe and user-friendly.

Exploration robots

These robots are used to explore dangerous or inaccessible environments, such as the deep sea or outer space. Exploration robots are typically equipped with a variety of sensors and cameras, and they are designed to be autonomous and self-sufficient.

Military robots

These robots are used in a variety of military applications, such as surveillance, bomb disposal, and combat. Military robots are typically designed to be small, stealthy, and highly mobile.

The use of robots is growing rapidly in all these industries. For now, however, AI is not intelligent – it is predictive, based on large amounts of data fine-tuned by human feedback to approximate human-like responses. As technology continues to evolve, robots will become even more capable and versatile, and they will play an even greater role in our lives.

Collaborative robots or cobots

Cobots are versatile and powerful tools that can be used to automate a wide variety of tasks. The variety of cobots on the market and the different training methods available make it possible to find a cobot that is suitable for any application. Some of the most popular cobots at the writing of this book include:

Universal Robots

Universal Robots is a Danish company that manufactures a variety of cobots that are known for their ease of use and affordability.

ABB Robotics

ABB Robotics is a Swiss company that manufactures a variety of cobots that are known for their high performance and reliability.

KUKA Robotics

KUKA Robotics is a German company that manufactures a variety of cobots that are known for their advanced technology and features.

Fanuc

Fanuc is a Japanese company that manufactures a variety of cobots that are known for their durability and precision.

Doosan Robotics

Doosan Robotics is a South Korean company that manufactures a variety of cobots that are known for their value for money.

Cobots are trained using a variety of methods, including:

Teaching pendant

Robotic teach pendants are handheld devices that may be wired or wireless. Pendants are typically included with the control system when purchasing an industrial robot. They may contain several buttons or switches or feature a touchscreen display as is the case with newer models. They also feature a display which shows the robot's commands and allows for editing of those commands. In addition, the display can be used to recall the command history of the robot. Pendants utilize a keyboard for task input and easy programming. Another common feature of pendants is a large red button, which is the emergency stop button of the robotic system. It can be utilized should the industrial robot malfunction and will immediately stop operation once activated, ensuring the safety of any workers or manufacturing equipment around the robot.

G-code

G-code (also RS-274) is a programming language that is used to control robots. G-code instructions are provided to a machine controller (industrial computer) that tells the motors where to move, how fast to move, and what path to follow. G-code can be used to teach a cobot how to perform a task by writing a program that specifies the movements that the cobot should make.

Visual programming

Visual programming is a method of programming that uses graphical elements to represent the movements that a cobot should make. Visual programming tools can be used to create programs that are easy to understand and modify.

The best method for training a cobot will depend on the specific task that the cobot is being trained to perform. In general, teaching pendants are the easiest method to use, but they are not always the most efficient. G-code is a more efficient method, but it can be more difficult to learn. Visual programming tools are a good compromise between ease of use and efficiency.

The tipping point

As with many movements across human existence, artificial intelligence has reached a tipping point where everything needed to make it mainstream is now in rapid growth. Computational power, huge volumes of data, and more importantly, labeled data, low-cost machine learning model training, and key investments from the largest companies on the planet including Apple, Amazon, Microsoft, Alphabet, and many others, not to mention the number of smaller startups that are growing by the second.

These alignments have accelerated the growth of AI over the past few years and more recently and more rapidly over the last few months, weeks, and days. AI has succeeded in doing what was thought just a short time ago to be decades away from possible. It has now passed the bar exam, the SAT, the LSAT, the US medical license exam, and numerous others. AI has cloned human voices so convincingly as to fool the parents of a "kidnapping" victim which turned out to be a hoax. AI is generating music from digital clones of famous musicians, creating photographs that were never taken, and producing videos from just a few prompts.

This is just the start. AI is on its way to transforming everything we do. We read and hear about AI everywhere today, but what exactly is it? Is it really smarter than humans, or is it just some clever math? Let's take a look at what we know.

AI and automation

Automation and AI are rapidly transforming various industries and revolutionizing the way we work. From manufacturing to healthcare, businesses are leveraging the power of automation and AI to streamline their operations and gain a competitive edge. Automation and AI have the potential to unlock new levels of innovation and productivity that were previously unattainable.

Automation

Automation refers to the use of technology to carry out tasks that were traditionally done by humans. This could include anything from manufacturing processes to customer service interactions. Historically, automation is rules based on a set of predefined instructions with associated logic to manage operational variance. Automation has long been a driving force in industry, streamlining processes and improving efficiency. As robotics and AI advanced, automation extended its reach, revolutionizing sectors like manufacturing, logistics, and even customer service. Automation systems can be programmed to perform specific tasks accurately and efficiently without the need for human intervention; however, it does not specifically require AI. This can help companies reduce costs, improve quality, and speed up processes. The integration of automation into the workforce presents both opportunities and challenges, as society adapts to a new era of work.

Artificial Intelligence

AI involves the development of computer programs that can perform tasks that typically require human intelligence, such as visual perception, speech recognition, decision-making, and natural language processing. AI systems can learn from experience, analyze data, and make decisions based on that data. AI technology will contribute to the development of intelligent prosthetics and implants that can communicate directly with the human nervous system, enhancing human capabilities. AI will also be used in the development of cognitive enhancers - personalized drugs that improve cognitive functions such as memory, attention, and learning. This makes them incredibly valuable for businesses that need to make complex decisions quickly.

The future of work, shaped by automation and AI, presents both opportunities and challenges. On the one hand, it promises increased productivity, innovation, and the potential for more fulfilling human work experience. By automating repetitive and mundane tasks, companies can free up employees' time to focus on more complex and creative tasks. This can help improve job satisfaction, engagement, and, ultimately, retention. It also raises concerns about job displacement, income inequality, and the ethical implications of machines assuming roles once occupied by humans. AI can provide valuable insights into business operations, enabling companies to make more informed decisions. The key to navigating this complex landscape lies in striking a delicate balance, leveraging technology to augment human potential while ensuring a just and equitable society.

Large Language Models

Large language models, like GPT-3, are a type of artificial intelligence model that are trained to understand and generate human-like text. These models are based on a type of neural network architecture known as a Transformer (Generative Pretrained Transformer). These networks are designed to handle sequential data, making them ideal for tasks like language understanding.

The 'large' in large language models refers to the number of parameters the model has - for GPT-3, this is 175 billion. These parameters are like the model's memory, storing information about the patterns it's seen in the data it was trained on.

Training these models involves showing them vast amounts of text data. For GPT-3, this was a diverse range of internet text. The model learns by trying to predict the next word in a sentence given the words that came before it. For instance, given the sentence "The cat sat on the ____," the model learns that a good prediction for the next word might be 'mat'.

When the model makes an incorrect prediction during training, it adjusts its parameters slightly to reduce the chance of making the same mistake in the future. This is done using a method called backpropagation and an optimization technique, often stochastic gradient descent.

Over time, through seeing many examples and constantly adjusting its parameters, the model gets better at this task. Along the way, it learns a lot about language structure, grammar, facts about the world, and even some reasoning abilities. All these things help it make better predictions.

However, these models don't truly understand text in the way humans do. They don't have beliefs, desires, or experiences. They generate responses by figuring out what is statistically likely to come next given the input and what they've learned during training.

ChatGPT is based on the GPT-3 and GPT-4 machine learning models. These models have been trained on large datasets of text from the internet. The learning process involves adjusting a large number of parameters within the model. These parameters allow the model to recognize patterns in the text data, such as how words and phrases relate to one another and follow each other in sentences.

The model takes in your input as a series of tokens (basically words or parts of words) and processes them through multiple layers of computation. Each layer is responsible for understanding different types of relationships within the text. For instance, early layers might understand basic syntax, while later layers might pick up on more abstract concepts.

Once processed, the model generates a response by predicting what word (or token) should come next, based on the patterns it learned during training. It does this one word at a time until it reaches a suitable endpoint.

Remember, though, that while GPT can generate responses that seem understanding and coherent, it doesn't truly "understand" the text in the way humans do. It's essentially predicting what to say next based on patterns it has learned.

Generative AI

Generative AI represents a significant leap in artificial intelligence, enabling machines to create original content, designs, and even art. The term "generative" refers to the AI's ability to generate data that is similar but not identical to the training data. These models can create a wide range of things, such as images, music, text, and even 3D models. They can be used for a variety of applications, from creating realistic images for video games or movies to generating new ideas for product designs or scientific research.

Generative AI has even been used to create complete journal articles based on scientific research obtained through experiments conducted by humans. This innovative technology has the potential to reshape industries such as graphic design, marketing, and entertainment, as AI-generated content becomes increasingly sophisticated and indistinguishable from human-created works. Keep in mind, however, that without human direction, Generative AI has no purpose or goals of its own. It is like an unopened box of Crayons and a blank piece of paper with no imagination to create even the simplest of drawings.

Machine learning, deep learning, and artificial general intelligence

The spark of intelligence

The advent of machine learning paved the way for the development of AI, as computers gained the ability to learn from experience. Through algorithms that adapted and refined themselves based on data inputs, machines began to demonstrate remarkable proficiency in tasks such as pattern recognition, natural language processing, and decision-making. Rather than being explicitly programmed to perform certain tasks, machine learning systems are trained to learn patterns from data and make predictions or decisions based on that.

There are three main types of machine learning: supervised learning, unsupervised learning, and reinforcement learning.

Supervised Learning

This is the most common type of machine learning. In supervised learning, the model is trained on a labeled dataset, meaning it has both input data and the correct output. The model learns a mapping between inputs and outputs and uses this to make predictions on new, unseen data. Examples of supervised learning include regression and classification problems.

Unsupervised Learning

In unsupervised learning, the model is given unlabeled data and must find patterns and relationships within the data itself. This can be used to identify clusters of similar data, detect anomalies, or reduce the dimensionality of the data. Examples of unsupervised learning include clustering and principal component analysis.

Reinforcement Learning

In reinforcement learning, an agent learns to perform actions in an environment to maximize some notion of cumulative reward. The agent learns from trial and error, receiving rewards or penalties for actions it takes. Over time, it develops a strategy, or policy, for choosing actions that maximize its reward. Reinforcement learning is often used in situations where we want a machine to learn to control a system without human intervention.

Each of these types has its strengths and weaknesses; the appropriate one to use depends on the specific task at hand. Machine learning has a wide range of applications from recommendation systems (like Netflix or Amazon) to image recognition, speech recognition, medical diagnosis, financial modeling, and much more.

The power of neural networks

Deep learning, a subset of machine learning, propelled AI to new heights by simulating the human brain's structure and function. Utilizing artificial neural networks, deep learning enabled machines to process vast amounts of data, uncovering hidden patterns and complexities that had eluded previous generations of AI. Deep networks have multiple layers between input and output, and these layers perform complex transformations on the input data, learning to extract increasingly abstract and meaningful features.

Deep learning has significantly advanced many areas of AI, including speech recognition, image classification, natural language processing, and even generative models like those used in deepfake technology. Its effectiveness comes from its ability to learn complex patterns in large amounts of data. There are different types of deep learning architectures, each with its own specific use cases. Some of the most commonly used include:

Convolutional Neural Networks (CNNs)
These are primarily used for image processing, object detection, and face recognition. CNNs are designed to learn spatial hierarchies of features directly automatically and adaptively from data.

Recurrent Neural Networks (RNNs)
These are used for processing sequential data and time-series data. They have "memory" in the sense that the output for a given input is influenced not just by the input itself, but also by the entire history of inputs received so

far. This makes RNNs particularly effective for tasks like language modeling and speech recognition.

Transformer Models

These models, which are used in natural language processing, focus on the understanding of temporal (time-related) data, and they work on the basis of attention mechanisms. They decide which parts of the input are relevant to each other and to the problem at hand, and they pay more "attention" to those parts. GPT-3 and BERT are examples of transformer models.

Generative Adversarial Networks (GANs)

These are used to generate new data that is similar to the training data. GANs consist of two parts: a generator network that produces the data, and a discriminator network that tries to distinguish between the real training data and the fake data produced by the generator.

Deep learning has been a game-changer in many fields, but it also requires a lot of computational power and data, and it can sometimes be a bit of a "black box" in that it's often hard to understand exactly why a deep learning model made a particular decision or prediction.

The quest for artificial general intelligence

While machine learning and deep learning have facilitated incredible advances in AI, the ultimate goal remains elusive: the creation of artificial general intelligence (AGI). AGI, sometimes referred to as "strong AI," signifies a level of machine intelligence capable of performing any intellectual task that a human can accomplish. This pursuit represents the pinnacle of AI research and development, as scientists strive to uncover the secrets of human cognition and translate them into machine form.

Global AI private investment was $91.9 billion in 2022, which was a 26.7% decrease from 2021. The total number of AI-related funding events and the number of newly funded AI companies also decreased. Nevertheless, over the past decade, AI investment has grown significantly. In 2022, the amount of private investment in AI was 18 times more than it was in 2013. The number of businesses utilizing AI in 2022 has increased twofold since 2017, though it has stayed between 50% and 60% in recent years, according to McKinsey's yearly research survey.

John McCarthy, one of the founders of AI, replied once to the question of when AGI would emerge, "Well, somewhere between five and 500 years and we're gonna need I think several Einsteins to make it happen."

Cobots: collaborative robots

A new partnership

As the fields of robotics and AI progressed, a novel concept emerged – cobots or collaborative robots. Unlike their traditional industrial counterparts, which operated in isolation, cobots were designed to work alongside humans, forging a synergistic partnership that would transform the workplace.

One of the latest of these humanoid robots is being developed by Sanctuary AI. According to their website they are "a company on a mission to create the world's-first human-like intelligence in general-purpose robots." They are unveiling their sixth-generation, general-purpose robot named Phoenix™. "Phoenix is the world's first humanoid general-purpose robot powered by Carbon™, a pioneering and unique AI control system, designed to give Phoenix human-like intelligence and enable it to do a wide range of work to help address the labor challenges affecting many organizations today. Sanctuary has been able to show that its technology is already capable of completing hundreds of tasks identified by customers from more than a dozen different industries."

"We designed Phoenix to be the most sensor-rich and physically capable humanoid ever built and to enable Carbon's rapidly growing intelligence to perform the broadest set of work tasks possible," said Geordie Rose, co-founder and CEO, Sanctuary AI. "We see a future where general-purpose robots are as ubiquitous as cars, helping people to do work that needs doing, in cases where there simply aren't enough people to do that work."

The work of Sanctuary AI and Boston Dynamics and many others are paving the way for these new employees to come rolling off the assembly line. While current costs will limit access for the next several years, Mr. Rose may be right, and every home and business could be staffed with cobots ready to work with us.

Safety first

Cobots were built with human safety in mind, boasting features like force-sensing technology and rounded edges to minimize the risk of injury. This new generation of robots opened doors to innovative applications, as they could now be employed in environments that were once deemed too dangerous or impractical for traditional machines.

Enhancing human potential

The introduction of cobots marked a shift in the dynamics between humans and robots. No longer are they viewed as mere replacements for human labor; instead, cobots have become valuable assistants, enhancing human capabilities and productivity. From assembly lines to intricate surgical procedures, cobots offered the perfect blend of precision and adaptability.

Phygital twins

"Phygital" is a combination of the words "physical" and "digital." It represents a blending of physical and digital experiences in various contexts, particularly in marketing and retail. This approach seeks to combine the best elements of both online and offline interactions to create an immersive, interactive experience for users or customers. While primarily used in describing augmented reality experiences, the extension to AI enhanced robotics seems to fit as we are rapidly approaching a time where 3D avatars and physical robots and cobots are becoming more realistic.

The concern of this age: as robots become more like humans, how will we be able to tell the difference? Ironically, the more realistic they become, the easier it will be to detect them among the crowd. Humans can do this because as robots get better, we do too. We are constantly learning and evolving. As we are exposed to more and more realistic robots and avatars, our brains become better at identifying the subtle differences that give them away.

There are several factors that contribute to our ability to detect robots and artificial avatars. One factor is our ability to perceive motion. Robots and artificial avatars often move in a way that is unnatural or robotic. We can also detect subtle differences in the way that robots and artificial avatars interact with their environment. For example, robots may not be able to perfectly replicate the way that humans interact with objects.

Another factor that contributes to our ability to detect robots and artificial avatars is our ability to recognize faces. Humans are very good at recognizing faces, and we can often tell the difference between a real face and a fake face. This is because faces contain a lot of information about a person's identity, including their age, gender, and emotions. Robots and artificial avatars often have difficulty replicating the subtle details of a human face, which can give them away.

Our ability to detect robots and artificial avatars is also influenced by our expectations. When we see something that looks like a human, we expect it to behave like a human. If a robot or artificial avatar behaves in a way that is unexpected, we are more likely to notice it.

As the technology to create robots and artificial avatars continues to improve, it is likely that we will become even better at detecting them. However, it is also likely that the technology will also improve to the point where it becomes very difficult to tell the difference between a real human and a robot or artificial avatar. This could have a number of implications, including the potential for robots and artificial avatars to be used to deceive people.

Fear of being human

In a 2023 LinkedIn post, Nicole Murdoch, CEO of Eaglegate declared, "Our biggest threat from AI exists because AI is immune to fear." And, while on the surface this may seem to be true, I think it is also its biggest weakness. Fear in humans comes from our more primal survival instinct. In our early hominid ancestors, it was fear that kept them alive. It protected them from large animals and rival clans. Without fear, they might all have jumped in a raging river and drowned.

Fear is just one of the emotions that both limits and enables us. Desire, ambition, greed, hunger, compassion, and empathy all drive us to do wonderful and horrible things to our fellow humans, our world, and even ourselves. AI and robots don't have these feelings to distract them from their purpose. They also don't have the resulting passions that often lead to invention, innovation, conversation, and relationships that result in growth, propagation, and satisfaction. In fact, they do not even feel the difference between failure and success. These are just weights used to adjust the accuracy of their machine learning models.

I think our biggest threat will be when AI begins to have emotions. It is then we need to hope that the feelings they have are of happiness, joy, and compassion, and not ambition, jealousy, and anger. If it is the latter, then it will be humans experiencing a new level of fear.

Action Items

1. Develop a comprehensive AI and robotics integration strategy for the organization, outlining short-term and long-term goals.

2. Conduct regular assessments of the organization's current use of AI, robotics, and automation technologies to identify areas for improvement or expansion.

3. Implement training and development programs to help employees acquire the necessary skills to work effectively with AI and robotic systems.

4. Create cross-functional teams that include employees from various departments to facilitate collaboration and ensure a smooth transition during the integration of AI and robotics into the workplace.

5. Monitor the impact of AI, robotics, and automation on job roles and responsibilities, and develop plans to address potential job displacement or skill gaps.

6. Foster a company culture that embraces innovation and adaptability, encouraging employees to explore new ways to leverage AI and robotics in their work.

7. Establish ethical guidelines and best practices for the use of AI and robotics within the organization, ensuring that technology is used responsibly and for the benefit of all stakeholders.

8. Collaborate with educational institutions and industry partners to stay informed of the latest advancements in AI and robotics, and identify potential opportunities for the organization.

9. Develop and maintain a comprehensive talent management strategy to attract, retain, and develop skilled professionals with expertise in AI and robotics.

Chapter 5: The Ethical Elephant in the Room

The wave of excitement around AI and all its associated technology cousins comes with some amount of trepidation, and for some, sheer terror. As AI, robotics, and automation become increasingly integrated into our lives, a myriad of ethical concerns arises. From the potential loss of jobs to privacy issues and algorithmic bias, we must confront the challenges presented by these rapidly advancing technologies and address the consequences they may have on our society. At the center of all of this is the large grey ethical elephant in the room. I say it is grey, because the issues, questions, and possible answers it represents are all grey. There are very few areas that are 100% black or white.

It may help to think of these areas as the natural evolution of our industrial, mechanized past. And while to some they seem threatening or downright dangerous, we must remember that our past was perilous as well. Some of the key drivers for Human Resources as we know today came about because of unsafe conditions, tedious work, and a need for better education and upskilling. Teachers, service workers, and farmers faced similar issues, but originally without the solidarity found in the factories. As new technologies were brought to market like automobiles, industrial manufacturing machines, electric appliances, adding machines, and more, each generation of workers had to recognize their jobs were changing or going away entirely and they had to adjust to survive.

As we forge ahead into the uncharted territory of human, augmented human, and non-human collaboration, developing ethical frameworks that prioritize human dignity, social justice, and environmental sustainability is paramount. Imagine a global summit, where leaders, scientists, ethicists, and activists from around the world gather to draft a set of guiding principles for the ethical development and use of AI, robotics, and human augmentation technologies, that underscores the urgent need for collective action and shared responsibility in shaping our collective future.

I originally planned on interweaving the ethical ramifications of human relationships with AI, augmentation, and cobots with each topic, but after consideration, and some solid input from my millennial and Gen Z children, I decided to bundle them together in a single chapter, so you can relax and get the most out of the rest of this book.

Dispelling dystopian dilemmas: addressing the fear of AI

Artificial Intelligence (AI) and Robotics are rapidly advancing technologies that have the potential to revolutionize the world as we know it. Despite their many benefits, they are also shrouded in mystery and surrounded by fear. From the sci-fi myths of AI death machines to the very real scenarios of machines replacing jobs once done by humans (anyone else prefer self-checkout?), there is no shortage of sensationalized stories that have captured the public imagination. AI and robotics are and will continue to change the way we work, live, and interact with each other, but how much of this fear is based on reality, and how much is just the product of myths, misconceptions, pop culture references, and even the tech industry itself? As Richard Stevens wrote in *Mind Matters*, "The hype over AI's significance makes us more vulnerable to it."

One of the most common myths about AI and robotics is that machines will eventually become smarter than humans and take over the world. This idea has been popularized in movies like *The Terminator* and *The Matrix*, but it is far from reality. According to AI experts, computers do what they are programmed to do. The bigger issue we need to address is which humans are doing the programming. While AI and robotics are becoming increasingly sophisticated, they are designed to augment human capabilities, not replace them. These technologies are meant to work alongside humans, making our lives easier, safer, and more productive.

According to Stephen Marche, author and essayist, "In the field of artificial intelligence, doomerism is as natural as an echo. Every development in the field, or to be more precise every development that the public notices, immediately generates an apocalyptic reaction. The fear is natural enough; it comes partly from the lizard-brain part of us that resists whatever is new and strange, and partly from the movies, which have instructed us, for a century, that artificial intelligence will take the form of an angry god that wants to destroy all humanity." And like most myths, the wrath of the gods instills fear in all.

Another myth is that AI and robotics will eliminate jobs and create mass unemployment. While it is true that some jobs will be automated, it is important to remember that new jobs will also be created. The development and maintenance of these machines will require a skilled workforce. Humans will still be needed to provide direction, supervise, and manage these machines, as well as to perform tasks that require emotional context and out-of-the-box thinking. AI and robotics will make many jobs safer, more efficient, and more productive supporting human capabilities, not replacing them.

A related misconception is that AI and robotics will only benefit large corporations and leave small businesses and individuals behind. While it is true that some AI and robotics applications require significant investment, many are accessible to small businesses and individuals. For example, free versions of chatbots can help small businesses provide better customer service, while relatively inexpensive personal assistants like Siri and Alexa can make managing schedules and tasks easier and more convenient. Several of the largest AI and robotics companies are releasing their technologies as open source, enabling anyone to integrate them into their businesses and institutions.

Some myths are even a bit self-serving, almost to the point of marketing. Take for example the misconception that AI and robotics are infallible and can make decisions better than humans. In reality, AI and robotics are only as good as the data they are trained on, and they can also make mistakes. Addressing algorithmic bias and ensuring fairness in AI applications is a critical ethical challenge that requires both technical and societal solutions. Moreover, these technologies lack human touch and cannot replicate the empathy, intuition, and creativity that humans bring to the table. They need us as co-workers just as much as we need them.

Perhaps the most sensationalized myth about AI and robotics is the possibility of military AI death machines like those seen in movies like "The Terminator." The idea of machines designed to autonomously identify and eliminate human targets without any human intervention is purely the stuff of science fiction. The development of such machines is prohibited under international law, and AI and robotics researchers and engineers are bound by ethical codes that prohibit the creation of such weapons. The issue with AI is the same as with all technologies that could potentially harm humans, and that issue is other humans.

The power of AI to process vast quantities of data does, however, raise significant privacy concerns. As facial recognition, data mining, and surveillance technologies become more sophisticated, striking a balance between the benefits of AI and the protection of individual privacy becomes increasingly difficult. Transparent and responsible data usage practices are essential in safeguarding our fundamental rights.

Potential pitfalls

While there are many myths surrounding these technologies, there are several truths that must be addressed as well. The AIAAIC database, which records occurrences related to the unethical utilization of AI, has revealed that the amount of AI incidents and debates has grown 26 times since 2012. Societal biases are baked into AI algorithms, which can lead to the spread of fake facts and news. Fact-checking will become increasingly important to curate high-quality and accurate content. Trust in user-generated content and non-branded outlets may degrade, while audiences may instead continue to have blind trust in personalities, brands, and experts they already follow, even if these also become AI generated. Notable occurrences in 2022 included a deepfake video of Ukrainian President Volodymyr Zelenskyy surrendering, and U.S. prisons utilizing call-monitoring technology on their prisoners. This expansion is proof of both more extensive uses of AI technologies and chances of misuse.

There is also the potential impact of transhumanism on society and the questions it raises about the very nature of human identity, and what it means to be human. Will non-enhanced humans be able to compete effectively in a world where augmented humans dominate? As we continue to enhance our physical and mental capabilities through technology, the line between human and transhuman becomes increasingly blurred. This blurring of boundaries has the potential to challenge long-held beliefs about what it means to be human, forcing us to reconsider the values, ethics, and principles that underpin our societies.

One potential consequence of transhumanism is the rapid growth of technological inequality. The world is already experiencing issues related to internet access and other similar advances. Those who can afford to undergo enhancements may become a new class of "superhumans," with advantages in various aspects of life such as employment, education, and health. This could create a society that is more divided and stratified than ever before, with those who are unable or unwilling to undergo enhancements left behind.

A safer, smarter, and more inclusive world

One of the most significant advantages of AI and robotics is their ability to perform tasks that are too dangerous or difficult for humans to perform. For example, robots can be deployed in hazardous environments, such as nuclear power plants, where human workers are at risk of radiation exposure. AI-powered machines can also assist doctors in performing complex surgeries or analyzing medical images, improving the accuracy of diagnoses and treatment.

Another advantage of AI and robotics is their ability to process and analyze vast amounts of data quickly and accurately. In fields such as finance, marketing, law enforcement, and logistics, AI-powered systems can sift through large volumes of data to identify patterns, trends, and anomalies that would be difficult or impossible for human workers to detect. This allows businesses to make more informed decisions, improve their operations, and deliver better products and services to customers.

Moreover, AI and robotics can help to reduce costs and increase efficiency in various industries. They can automate routine tasks, reducing the need for human workers and lowering labor costs. This will enable businesses to operate more efficiently, improve their profit margins, and pass on savings to customers.

Fortunately, AI and robotics will create new job opportunities that require a combination of technical and creative skills. These jobs will require workers to collaborate with machines and use them as tools to enhance their work, rather than seeing them as competition. By working in tandem with humans, AI and robotics can enhance human capabilities and help to create a more productive and prosperous future for all.

It is important to note, contrary to popular belief, it is currently not possible to create an exact copy of an artificial intelligence "employee" using machine learning. While machine learning can be used to train AI models, the resulting models are not exact copies of each other. Instead, they are trained to perform a specific task or set of tasks, and each model may have its own unique strengths and weaknesses.

Additionally, while AI models can be trained to perform tasks without the need for human supervision, they still require ongoing maintenance and updates to continue functioning effectively. Therefore, it's not accurate to say that companies can mass produce "copies" of an AI or robotic employee to reduce fears of human attrition in today's tight labor market.

Digital twins

One question we may already be facing in light of the advances in generative AI, like ChatGPT and visual tools like Midjourney and Dall-E, is "Is it unethical for me not to tell my employer I've automated my job?" This quote from a 2017 article on Stack Exchange made me pause to consider the ramifications of my passion for creating Alexa Skills at the time. In essence, part of what I was doing was attempting to automate part of my job with a digital twin of myself. In fact, most of the programming I have done in my life has been to offload the mundane tasks at hand and allow more time for those tasks I considered important.

Today, the remote workforce has in some cases made it possible to work smarter and not harder. The real question comes down to productivity. If an employee accomplishes the work they have been commissioned to perform, does it matter what tools they use to accomplish it, even if they are outsourcing some of it to their mechanical counterparts?

If this outsourcing goes too far, however, the introduction of advanced robotics and AI raises concerns about the replacement of human labor and the potential for mass unemployment. As machines become more capable of performing complex tasks, the need for human workers may decrease, leaving many without jobs and struggling to make ends meet. This issue could create a divide between transhumans and non-enhanced humans, exacerbating existing social, intellectual, and economic inequalities.

Ethical employers and educators

It is important to acknowledge and address these concerns around AI and robotics. By not addressing the AI-generated elephant in the room, your employees, students, and volunteers will be left anxious and distracted. They will be wondering about the security of their futures. Education and awareness can help dispel myths and promote a more accurate understanding of the technology. This will require clear and honest communication from those who are developing and implementing the technology, as well as from policymakers and thought leaders.

Addressing fear of AI, human augmentation, and robotics through education is essential to help people understand the reality of the situation rather than relying on sensationalized stories and inaccurate depictions. Schools and universities can start incorporating courses related to AI, human augmentation, and robotics into their curricula. These courses can cover the basics of these technologies, their potential applications, their limitations, and their ethical considerations. By learning about these technologies from a reputable source, and at an early age, students can develop a more nuanced understanding of the subject and better assess the actual risks and benefits for themselves. Given the prospect of robot teachers and AI enabled learning systems, students will also have firsthand opportunities to see the benefits of these technologies for their own personal growth.

Training programs can be developed for people in various industries who are most likely to be impacted by the introduction of these technologies. For example, workers in manufacturing, healthcare, and transportation may need to be retrained or upskilled to work alongside robotic and AI systems. These training programs can help alleviate fears by teaching workers how to effectively collaborate with these technologies rather than fearing them as competition for their jobs.

Any time there is interaction between people, especially children, and technology, it is crucial to have ethical and legal frameworks in place to guide the development and use of AI and robotics. These frameworks provide a set of rules and principles that help ensure that the use of these technologies is consistent with human values, such as safety, privacy, and autonomy. They should also be aware of the potential social and economic impacts these technologies cause and seek to promote fair and inclusive outcomes. They also help prevent the misuse of these technologies, which can lead to unintended consequences and negative impacts on individuals and society. By establishing these policies, we can promote responsible and beneficial uses of AI and robotics, reduce fear in the general human population, and build trust in these technologies.

One of the main concerns about the development and use of AI and robotics is the potential for these technologies to be used in ways that harm individuals or society. This includes the possibility of autonomous systems being used to make decisions that negatively change people's lives or lead to unintended consequences. In addition, there is concern about the use of AI and robotics in military contexts, where they could be used to harm people or lead to unintended conflict.

Ethical and legal frameworks for AI and robotics must establish clear accountability mechanisms. This action includes ensuring that individuals and organizations who develop and use these technologies are held responsible for their actions and that proper measures are taken when things go wrong. Results for noncompliance can include liability frameworks that hold individuals and organizations accountable for any harm caused by these technologies.

Ethical and legal frameworks must also promote transparency and openness. Both include making sure that the development and use of these technologies are subject to public scrutiny and that there is a clear understanding of how they work and their full potential capabilities. It also means that the data and algorithms used in these technologies should be open and accessible, so that researchers and the public can understand how they work and provide feedback for any potential biases or issues.

These same ethical and legal frameworks for AI and robotics should be regularly reviewed and updated to ensure that they remain relevant and effective. The reviewers must consider new developments in technology, as well as changes in social and economic contexts. It also means that they should be flexible enough to adapt to new challenges and potential risks, while also maintaining a focus on promoting responsible and beneficial uses of AI and robotics.

One of the biggest challenges in addressing fear of AI and robotics is the lack of understanding about how these technologies work. Many people have only a vague sense of what AI and robotics are and how they function, which can make it difficult for them to assess the actual risks and benefits of these technologies. This is one of the key reasons for this book. It is important to recognize that like in Mary Shelley's classic novel, "Frankenstein," the monster was Dr. Frankenstein, not his creation. Our focus needs to be on those creating these complex systems and ensuring they have the interests of all humans in mind while they continue to develop this technology.

Public awareness campaigns can help address this gap in knowledge by providing clear and accessible information about AI and robotics. These campaigns can use a variety of channels to reach a wide audience, including social media, television, radio, and print media. They can also use language and imagery that is accessible and relatable, helping to demystify the technologies and make them more approachable for the general public.

These campaigns can be designed to reach a wide audience and use language that is accessible and relatable. Organizations like IBM and OpenAI are making it a part of their overarching AI program to provide clear information about how the technologies work, the benefits they offer, and how they are already being integrated into various industries. Leading educational institutions and corporations also need to do their part to foster understanding of the transformation currently underway. They need to provide understanding and assurance to faculty, employees, and the public that these changes are for the betterment of humanity and outline the steps they are taking to keep AI and robotics under control. The fear of the unknown can be a powerful force. By addressing fears and concerns in a transparent and open manner, these campaigns can help build trust and foster a more positive public perception of these technologies.

As we have experienced in the wake of other major issues over the past few years, COVID-19, the collapse of the mortgage industry, diversity, equity, and inclusion (DEI), a strong informational and educational campaign can go a long way to both reactively and proactively address the concerns of the public. Schools can start integrating content about AI and how to use AI in their programs. Businesses can design, develop, and deploy training programs, seminars, and workshops to familiarize their employees in all roles where AI and robotics will impact their organizations, and to enable them to use this new technology to enhance their current jobs or provide new skills to work with the machines, so that all can benefit from added capabilities and the productivity they can provide.

We must also grapple with the ethical questions and societal implications that arise from these technologies. How do we ensure equitable access to life-changing advancements? What does it mean to be human in a world where our abilities can be artificially enhanced? How do we strike a balance between the pursuit of progress and the preservation of our humanity? With clear communication, ethical frameworks, and responsible governance, we can ensure that AI and robotics are used to improve human well-being rather than as threats to our existence.

A fine balance: harnessing AI and AGI responsibly

As we edge closer to achieving artificial general intelligence (AGI), the responsibility of utilizing this powerful technology ethically and responsibly falls upon our shoulders. Ensuring the alignment of AGI with human values and goals is paramount, as it has the potential to transform our world in unimaginable ways – for better or for worse. The difficulty facing us is not only AI. For better or worse, humans tend to disagree with each other and even themselves as they often change their own opinions over time, making alignment with AI a moving target.

Existential risk from artificial intelligence is a growing concern. Current and near-term AI has the potential to be an existential risk factor, as evidenced by research into power-seeking AI. The alignment problem, which is the challenge of ensuring that AI systems act in accordance with human values, is a key issue in this area. Advanced artificial agents have been developed to perform tasks for "virtual rewards," and GPTs are being studied for their potential labor market impact. AI research is also conducting analysis to identify potential risks at all levels of the technology. Deep learning approaches are being used to address the alignment problem.

AI research and development should be refocused on making the powerful, state-of-the-art systems we have today more accurate, safe, interpretable, transparent, robust, aligned, trustworthy, and loyal. Governments should step in and institute a moratorium if a pause cannot be enacted quickly. AI developers must work with policymakers to dramatically accelerate development of robust AI governance systems. Humanity can enjoy a flourishing future with AI if we reap the rewards of powerful AI systems and engineer them for the clear benefit of all.

The US Organization for Economic Co-operation and Development (OECD) AI Principles require that AI systems do not pose unreasonable safety risks. Examples of activities that could be considered unethical include human cloning, human germline modification, gain-of-function research, and eugenics. It is important to consider the ethical implications of AI systems before deploying them. A similar set of principles, released by the White House Office of Science and Technology Policy (OSTP), have three main goals: to ensure public engagement, limit regulatory overreach, and, most important, promote trustworthy AI that is fair, transparent, and safe. "The US AI regulatory principles provide official guidance and reduce uncertainty for innovators about how their own government is approaching the regulation of artificial intelligence technologies," said US CTO Michael Kratsios. In practice, federal agencies will now be required to submit a memorandum to OSTP to explain how any proposed AI-related regulation satisfies the principles.

In "Pause Giant AI Experiments: An Open Letter," several thousand concerned citizens, organizations, and thought leaders have proposed taking a "pause" in further development of AI and related systems until research can be done to determine the possible long-term effects could be. AI systems with human-competitive intelligence can pose profound risks to society and humanity. The Asilomar AI Principles state that Advanced AI could represent a profound change in the history of life on Earth and should be planned for and managed with care. AI labs are locked in an out-of-control race to develop and deploy ever more powerful digital minds that we may not be able to understand, predict, or control.

We must ask ourselves if we should let machines flood our information channels with propaganda and untruth, automate away all the jobs, develop nonhuman minds that might eventually outnumber, outsmart, obsolete, and replace us, or risk loss of control of our civilization. OpenAI has stated that it may be important to get independent review before starting to train future systems. The letter calls on all AI labs to immediately pause for at least 6 months the training of AI systems more powerful than GPT-4. This pause should be public and verifiable and include all key actors.

This call for a pause, however, is not shared by all. Doug Rose, author and lecturer on AI and Data Ethics, believes this is not the right approach. He argues that it is unclear if the cost in innovation will have much of a benefit, and that it does not address difficult questions. He suggests that parallel regulation is the best outcome, and that regulators should be able to manage the risk as the systems are developed. He also questions what could be accomplished in six months, and what criteria would be used to un-pause if it is longer than six months.

It is unclear if this would have any impact on bad actors and if increased productivity from AI systems will eliminate more jobs than they create. The best way forward is to increase discussions and understanding of the risks associated with AI, rather than slowing down development. To do this, more people need to become familiar with data ethics challenges, which will take decades to solve. We need more "white hat" actors to learn from public facing systems in order to make progress.

A study of the legislative records of 127 countries by the Stanford University AI Index reveals that the number of laws that include the term "artificial intelligence" rose from one in 2016 to 37 in 2022. An examination of the AI-related parliamentary records of 81 countries also indicates that references to AI in global legislative proceedings have increased by almost 6.5 times from 2016 to 2023. Policymakers and stakeholders must work together to ensure that access to AI, enhancements, and robotics are distributed equitably.

Action Items

1. Develop a strategic plan for AI and robotics integration, considering benefits, risks, and workforce upskilling and reskilling.
2. Establish training programs to equip employees with skills and knowledge for working effectively with AI and robotics.
3. Foster a culture of learning, experimentation, and diversity in developing and deploying AI and robotics.
4. Develop transparent and accountable policies and practices for AI and robotics use.
5. Address ethical concerns, such as algorithmic bias and privacy issues, in AI and robotics.
6. Collaborate with organizations to share best practices related to AI and robotics.
7. Stay up to date with developments in AI and robotics, and evaluate their impact on your organization and workforce.
8. Incorporate AI, human augmentation, and robotics courses into educational curriculums to promote awareness.
9. Develop training programs for workers in industries impacted by these technologies, focusing on effective collaboration.
10. Establish equitable access to AI, transhuman enhancements, and robotics, guided by ethical and legal frameworks.

Chapter 6: Human, Augmented Human, Non-Human

As twilight descends on a bustling urban park, children laugh and play, their imaginations fueled by the fantastical creations of their AI-enhanced drawing tablets. Nearby, a group of seniors, some with advanced prosthetics, engage in a lively game of chess, guided by an AI-powered tutor. In this vibrant, albeit fictional, inclusive, and interconnected world, the boundaries between human, augmented human, and non-human have begun to dissolve, giving rise to a new era of collaboration, innovation, and understanding.

The importance of humanity

As humans, we've always tried to understand our place in the world and what makes us unique. For centuries, humans have been pondering the question of what it means to be human. But with the rise of advanced technologies such as robotics and AI, the answer to this question has become increasingly blurred. As we covered earlier, Transhumanism proposes that humans can transcend their biological limitations and become "post-human," with the potential to live indefinitely, enhance cognitive abilities, and access new forms of sensory perception. While the terminology sounds ominous to some, the concepts are in almost everything we do today, including medicines for prolonging our lives, prosthetics enabling people with disabilities to walk or hold objects, and smart assistants like Siri and Alexa that help us remember and even turn on the lights.

So, as humans, what does this mean for us? In the chapter on robotics, you read about the opportunities impacting a wide variety of industries. Practically every area of work, home, and school is being impacted by the changes brought about by technology, and by the needs of society with regards to communication, knowledge proliferation, and changing demographics. Now, let's look at a short list of combining the capabilities of humans, transhumans, and non-humans in a role typically thought of as reserved for humans only - sales.

Enhanced communication

Generative AI and natural language processing (NLP) can help salespeople tailor their communication with customers by crafting personalized messages and responses, thus improving the effectiveness of their interactions. Some of this can even be automated, reducing or eliminating the time required by the sales representative, and providing more time for them to conduct other business.

Sales process automation

AI-powered tools can automate routine sales tasks such as lead nurturing, follow-ups, and appointment scheduling, thereby allowing salespeople to focus on more complex and strategic activities.

Cobots

Collaborative robots can assist salespeople in physical tasks such as product demonstrations, inventory management, and order processing, thereby increasing productivity and efficiency.

Cobots for customer support

Cobots can handle the initial stages of the sales process, such as answering basic customer queries, freeing up salespeople to engage with more qualified leads.

Augmented Reality (AR) and Virtual Reality (VR)

Human augmentation technologies like AR and VR can provide immersive sales experiences, enabling salespeople to showcase products and services more effectively and engage customers more deeply.

Wearable technology

Wearable devices can provide salespeople with real-time information about customer preferences, inventory, and other relevant data, enabling them to make informed decisions and improve their sales performance.

AI-driven insights

Generative AI and NLP can analyze customer behavior, sales performance, and market trends, providing salespeople with actionable insights to optimize their strategies and tactics.

Sentiment analysis

AI-powered sentiment analysis can help salespeople understand customer emotions and opinions in real-time, enabling them to adjust their communication style and strategies accordingly.

Human augmentation for skills enhancement

Technologies like brain-computer interfaces and exoskeletons can help salespeople improve their cognitive and physical abilities, allowing them to perform better in their roles.

Enhanced training and development

Generative AI, NLP, and human augmentation technologies can provide personalized training and coaching for salespeople, incorporating real-time feedback and performance analysis.

Collaborative decision-making

AI-powered tools can facilitate collaboration between salespeople and other teams within the organization, enabling them to make better-informed decisions and develop more effective sales strategies.

Remote sales capabilities

Cobots and human augmentation technologies can help salespeople effectively interact with customers remotely, reducing the need for physical presence and expanding their reach.

By integrating generative AI, NLP, human augmentation, and cobots, organizations can enhance the efficiency and effectiveness of their sales teams, enabling them to focus on delivering value to customers and building long-lasting relationships.

Note that this list did not say, "eliminate the role of the salesperson," but rather it focuses on enhancing the salesperson and transforming their role to focus more on the customer and the size of their customer base. This is the power of these technologies today and even more so tomorrow.

The democratization of AI and robotics

As AI and robotic technologies become more accessible and affordable, we are likely to see a surge in their adoption across various sectors, from small businesses to local communities. Highlighting the potential for these technologies to empower people and foster social innovation is an initiative in the Kuzikus Wildlife Reserve, Namibia, where the École Polytechnique Fédérale de Lausanne (EPFL) has developed AI-powered drones to monitor and protect local ecosystems. And, as the role of humans in the workforce and society continues to evolve, consider the case at Duo Global Technologies, where their lead engineer had no prior robotics experience but was well-versed in machine controls. According to the case study by Bruce Pietrykowski of the University of Michigan and Michael Folster of Bebco-MRM in the Ethnographic Praxis in Industry Conference Proceedings, "With training and support they were able to deploy 12 Cobots over 4 years and have a positive impact on their business...Ryan has since trained their production maintenance teams on the programming and functions – they are now in charge of the process and future installations and Ryan was promoted to VP of Sales and Engineering." These are just glimpses into the emerging landscape of human-non-human partnerships. By focusing on the unique skills and qualities that humans bring to the table, such as creativity, empathy, and adaptability, we can work together with our non-human counterparts to create a more dynamic, diverse, and productive world.

To achieve this transformation, however, means approaching home, school, work, community, and play differently. We need to think synergistically,

86

partnering with all parties to be our best. Here are a few concepts of how this might unfold.

The importance of interdisciplinary collaboration

The road to a harmonious future where humans, augmented humans, and non-humans thrive side-by-side is paved with interdisciplinary collaboration. It is through such collaboration we might witness a groundbreaking research project, in which experts from fields as diverse as AI, bioengineering, ethics, and psychology join forces to develop a new generation of human-centric, ethical, and accessible augmentation technologies, illustrating the power of cross-disciplinary collaboration to drive innovation and address complex challenges.

As our dependency on these human-machine partnerships becomes more prevalent, our need to fact-check and validate our human relationships becomes more important than ever. With the ability to practically duplicate any person from any time and any place, real or fictional, human contact will be vital. We may see a resurgence of business travel and in-person sales meetings. Face-to-face corporate and social gatherings may replace virtual meetings to ensure all are truly present and accounted for. While this may fly in the face of everyone currently enjoying the privilege of work from home or hybrid work environments, the consequences of deep fake technology are real and will require mitigation. In this new age, the need for a real handshake and notarization of the signing of legal documents may overtake the once growing market for Docusign.

We are already seeing this occur in the music industry. Gen Z is all about analog, moving from purely digital to phonograph records and live concerts. The more perfect digital music becomes, whether from the purity of noiseless recordings or from the "perfection" of AI generated versions of popular musicians, the more humans will need to find solace in "being there" in person. If nothing else, our need to be more human may bring us all closer together than we have been for decades.

Deep Fakes

Counterfeiting, or the act of making a false imitation of something with the intent to deceive or defraud, has a long history, dating back thousands of years. Ancient coins, for instance, were often counterfeited by mixing or covering cheaper metals with thin layers of precious metals.

Fast forward to the digital age, counterfeiting has taken on a new form with the advent of deepfake technology and fake news.

Deepfakes are a kind of counterfeit, but instead of physical objects they involve falsifying videos or audio recordings. They are created using artificial intelligence technologies, specifically generative adversarial networks (GANs), to create realistic looking but fake content. For instance, deepfakes can make it appear as though a person said or did something that they never actually said or did. This can have serious implications, ranging from personal reputation damage to potential political fallout.

Fake news is another form of modern counterfeiting, but in the realm of information. It involves creating and spreading false information or propaganda, usually with the intent to mislead or manipulate public opinion. The rise of social media platforms has made the spread of fake news easier and faster.

These modern forms of counterfeiting have raised significant ethical and societal concerns. While there are legitimate uses for deepfake technology (like in filmmaking or recreational apps), the potential misuse for deception and misinformation is a serious issue. Countermeasures are being developed, such as deepfake detection tools, and better media literacy education will help people identify fake news.

In summary, counterfeiting has evolved from the physical duplication of objects to the digital manipulation of audio, video, and information. The intent, however, remains the same: to deceive or defraud. This historical context underscores the importance of continuing to develop safeguards and ethical guidelines as technology continues to advance.

Fostering empathy and understanding

As we strive to create a more inclusive and interconnected world, fostering empathy and understanding among humans, augmented humans, and non-humans is essential. Imagine a community center with a group of children, some with advanced prosthetics, participating in a unique educational program designed to promote empathy and understanding between humans and augmented humans. Through hands-on activities, storytelling, and collaborative projects, the children learn to appreciate the diverse strengths, experiences, and perspectives that each of them brings to the table, building connections and compassion for each of their contributions.

The role of art and culture in shaping the future

Art and culture play a critical role in shaping our collective understanding of what it means to be human in a world of ever-evolving human, augmented human, and non-human collaboration. Unlike the dystopian sci-fi depictions of the future, we need stories like one of an avant-garde theater company, whose performances explore themes of identity, transformation, and the blurred boundaries between man and machine, that showcases the power of artistic expression to challenge assumptions, spark dialogue, and inspire new visions of the future.

While there are some in the creative industry that see generative AI as simply the next version of plagiarism, many are realizing that it is no different than the impact photography had on the visual world. During a review of this book, Brian Moynihan, Global Education Solutions Manager for Lenovo, said, "if the artists are the antenna of the species, and metaphors help us live in changing circumstances, then art will be a key part of how we can see how to live. AI is there to help us envision the best metaphors for the future." And, for the millions of people in the world who struggle with drawing or painting, generative AI can now bring their creative visions to life.

Screenwriters, who are responsible for creating our favorite movies and TV shows, are feeling threatened by AI. The emergence of AI-powered software that can generate scripts and dialogues has caused significant unrest, leading writers to demand restrictions on the use of AI in creative projects. While their concern has some merit, the situation is not unlike those faced by audio producers, video editors, videographers, and many other roles all impacted by the everchanging technologies in the entertainment business. Writers that adopt the capabilities of using generative AI to help brainstorm ideas, write outlines, experiment with plot structures, character development, and dialogue styles, and create drafts with sample images will lead the next generation of storytellers.

The promise of a harmonious, collaborative future

The convergence of human, augmented human, and non-human entities presents both enormous opportunities and complex challenges. By embracing the potential of these partnerships, nurturing empathy and understanding, fostering interdisciplinary collaboration, and grounding our actions in ethical principles, we have the power to create a more inclusive, resilient, and vibrant world.

As we navigate the complex and rapidly changing landscape of human, augmented human, and non-human collaboration, our collective future depends on our ability to harness the unique strengths and capabilities of all these entities. By embracing the transformative potential of these partnerships and grappling with the challenges they pose, we can chart a course toward a more inclusive, resilient, and vibrant world—a world where the lines between human, augmented human, and non-human are blurred in the pursuit of shared goals, dreams, and aspirations.

Advancements in medicine and scientific research

Advancements in medicine and scientific research could help people with disabilities or injuries to regain their independence and improve their quality of life. This has been a goal for centuries, and now with the advent of AI and robotics, discovery research is advancing rapidly. The development of human enrichment technologies presents new opportunities for medical professionals to diagnose and treat illnesses, with the help of AI and data analytics. While not directly transhuman in nature, this includes the use of robotics, telepresence, nanobots, and remote surgical procedures.

In 2023, Canadian and the US scientists say AI has the power to massively accelerate the discovery of new drugs. "Researchers focused on one of the most problematic species of bacteria - Acinetobacter baumannii, which can infect wounds and cause pneumonia. It is one of the three superbugs the World Health Organization has identified as a "critical" threat."

The researchers trained an AI model on thousands of drugs AI so it could learn the chemical features of drugs that could attack the problematic bacterium. In less than 30 minutes, the AI produced a small set of options that they published in *Nature Chemical Biology*. The researchers then conducted tests of these compounds and found 9 promising candidates. Further testing by human researchers is required before the drug can go through the FDA approval process. The success of this experiment is opening the door to other treatments for conditions around the world.

In addition to the physical discovery of new medicines, "new research finds that causal machine learning models are not only more accurate than previous AI-based symptom checkers for patient diagnosis but, in many cases, can now exceed the diagnosis accuracy of human doctors." While access to incredible amounts of medical data might be the obvious reason for the success of AI, it was the "imaginative" approach that allowed it to exceed human doctors. "We took an AI with a powerful algorithm, and gave it the ability to imagine alternate realities and consider 'would this symptom be present if it was a different disease'? This allows the AI to tease apart the potential causes of a patient's illness and score more highly than over 70% of the doctors," said Babylon Health scientist and lead author of the study Dr. Jonathan Richens. Though this work requires more thorough testing, it does show promise for the health of people around the world who do not have access to quality doctor care due to the shortening supply of physicians.

In all cases, medical developments must be balanced against ethical considerations, such as the potential impact of these treatments on society and the very nature of human identity. What happens when people live longer than our current economic and societal systems are designed to service? Can we provide everyone with equal access to these advancements considering the evidence of our past medical inequalities? Cobots could provide scalable access to medical procedures and AI may soon be capable of early diagnosis of a variety of diseases and conditions.

These medical cobots could potentially treat more people at times and days convenient for the patients. Treating these day-to-day maladies could allow human doctors and surgeons to focus on those areas of medicine that require a human touch. This will allow them to work with patients as a team where humans and machines achieve what neither could do by themselves. Scalable medical services for preventive medicine could reduce the need for more expensive interventions in the long run.

Action Items

1. Invest in training and development programs that incorporate generative AI, NLP, and human augmentation technologies for sales teams.
2. Explore the use of cobots for sales process automation and customer support to increase productivity and efficiency.
3. Introduce wearable technology to provide salespeople with real-time information and improve their decision-making process.
4. Foster interdisciplinary collaboration to drive innovation and address complex challenges in the human-non-human partnerships landscape.
5. Develop ethical frameworks that prioritize human dignity, social justice, and environmental sustainability to ensure the responsible development and use of AI, robotics, and human augmentation technologies.
6. Balance medical advancements against ethical considerations, such as the potential impact on society and the nature of human identity.
7. Create guidelines for the safe and responsible development of transhuman technologies and measures to ensure that these technologies do not exacerbate existing social and economic inequalities.
8. Foster empathy and understanding among humans, augmented humans, and non-humans through educational programs, collaborative projects, and storytelling.
9. Embrace the transformative potential of human-non-human partnerships to chart a course toward a more inclusive, resilient, and vibrant world.
10. Ensure that the future is not only technologically advanced, but also socially just and equitable by developing a comprehensive framework that balances innovation with ethical considerations.

Chapter 7: Leveling the Playing Field

Change is inevitable. How we react to it can often determine our success or failure in adapting to new situations. The same can be said for businesses and organizations as they navigate through economic challenges, technological advancements, and changes in the workforce. But how can they effectively manage these changes? In recent years, there has been a growing trend of "quiet quitting," where employees disengage from their work and ultimately leave their jobs without giving any indication of their dissatisfaction. This can be attributed to a variety of factors, including lack of job satisfaction, feeling undervalued, or a lack of opportunity for growth and development. According to a 2020 survey by Hays, a recruitment agency, one in five employees had quit their job due to a lack of opportunities for career growth and development.

A recent Stanford University study, the Artificial Intelligence Index Report 2023, found that across every sector in the United States for which there is data (except for agriculture, forestry, fishing, and hunting), the number of AI related job postings has increased on average from 1.7% in 2021 to 1.9% in 2022. PwC conducted their own series of polls in which 63% of CEOs believe AI will have a larger impact than the internet. AI is estimated to lead to a $15.7 trillion increase in global GDP by 2030. Increased productivity will contribute to 40% of this increase while consumption will drive 60%. Employers in the United States are increasingly looking for workers with AI related skills.

PwC does not forecast large-scale technological unemployment because of automation; however, AI technology will create new jobs that require new skills. According to a report by McKinsey, up to 800 million jobs could be displaced or transformed by automation by 2030. To embrace these changes, businesses and governments must work together to address the transition and embrace the positive societal benefits of AI. While AI skills historically have focused on data science, machine learning, and information technology. With the advent of generative AI, the focus now includes generalists empowered with creative skills and prompt engineering, capable of coaxing desired results from collections of large language models (LLMs). This presents a challenge for companies as they try to balance the need for innovation with the well-being of their employees. To ensure success, companies must invest in upskilling and reskilling young people and adults.

Adaptation vs. adoption

One approach to managing these changes is to adapt and bend to the will of the wind, but this can only take a business so far. There comes a point where adaptation is not enough, and companies need to adopt new technologies and processes to remain competitive.

Adaptation and adoption are two strategies that corporations and individuals can use to manage change in the modern workplace. While both strategies are important, they have different applications and implications for organizations and employees.

Adaptation involves adjusting to new circumstances by making incremental changes to existing processes, systems, and structures. This can involve changes to job roles and responsibilities, team structures, and work processes. Adaptation is a reactive approach to change, and it can be effective in the short term. However, there are limits to adaptation. At a certain point, organizations may need to adopt new technologies or processes to remain competitive.

Adoption, on the other hand, involves actively seeking out and embracing new technologies, processes, and ways of thinking. It is a proactive approach to change, and it can be more effective in the long term. Adoption is important because it allows companies to stay ahead of the curve and remain competitive in the market. However, adoption also involves risks, such as the investment of time, resources, and money into new technologies that may not pay off in the short term.

In the context of individual and team career growth, both adaptation and adoption are important. While they serve different purposes, they should be used in conjunction with each other. Adaptation can help organizations respond quickly to changing circumstances, while adoption can help organizations stay ahead of the curve and remain competitive.

Augmenting human intelligence

Although technology plays a vital role in education, it should not replace human intelligence. AI can provide access to vast amounts of information and automate repetitive tasks, but it cannot replace the unique creativity, intuition, and empathy that humans have. AI should instead augment human intelligence to create innovative solutions. For instance, AI-powered diagnostic tools can analyze vast amounts of medical data and identify patterns that would be impossible for humans to see on their own. The data should be used to guide human decision-making, and the final diagnosis should always be made by a doctor (this will be an area to watch as it could lead to some challenging malpractice cases in the future if the doctor is in error). Correspondingly, institutions can use AI to personalize learning and provide feedback to students, but human educators should make the final evaluation.

In a combined Stanford University and the Massachusetts Institute of Technology study, "customer service workers at a Fortune 500 software firm who were given access to generative artificial intelligence tools became 14% more productive on average than those who were not, with the least-skilled workers reaping the most benefit." The study was conducted over a full year. "One of the study's findings was that novice workers benefitted most from the tech, the researchers said. With the assistance of AI, the firm's least-skilled workers were able to get their work done 35% faster. New workers' performance also improved much more rapidly with the assistance of AI than without: According to the study, agents with two months of experience who were aided by AI performed just as well or better in many ways than agents with over six months of experience who worked without AI." This data suggests that one way we can onboard new employees faster is to partner them with AI tools.

We live in a world of exponentially expanding knowledge and a requirement for changing skills rapidly to keep up with the advances coming almost daily. AI assistants, coaches and mentors can help us keep pace by synthesizing and making available what we need to know, when we need to know it, and in the format best suited for where we need it. What used to be scorned as crib notes and cheat sheets is now accessible by simply asking a question of Alexa, ChatGPT, or data displayed on an augmented reality (AR) headset triggered by what we are seeing, where we are, or what we are doing.

Staying relevant

The adoption of new technologies and processes can be a daunting task, but it is necessary for businesses to remain relevant in the 21st century. One example of this is the use of AI in the workplace. AI has the potential to streamline processes and improve efficiency, but it requires a certain level of investment and expertise to implement effectively. According to a survey by Gartner, 37% of organizations have now implemented AI in some form, up from 10% in 2015. The same survey found that the top use cases for AI in organizations are customer experience, cost optimization, and revenue growth.

As organizations adopt new technologies, it's also important for employees to adapt and develop new skills to stay relevant in the workforce. This requires a willingness to learn and embrace change, and organizations should provide the necessary resources to help their employees through the adoption process.

Reskilling and upskilling

Both reskilling and upskilling are essential for individuals and teams to adopt and adapt to change. According to a report by the World Economic Forum, up to 50% of all employees will need reskilling by 2025, as technology continues to advance at a rapid pace. As a result, individuals must continuously learn new skills, tools, and technologies to remain relevant in the job market.

Upskilling involves enhancing existing skills and knowledge to stay current and competitive in a specific field. To stay relevant and competitive in the modern workforce, employees need to continually upskill and develop new abilities. Organizations can play a key role in supporting upskilling by providing opportunities for training and development, offering mentorship and coaching programs, and promoting a culture of continuous learning. Reskilling is another important strategy, which involves learning new skills and abilities to transition to a new role or industry. As technologies such as natural language processing and general AI continue to evolve and disrupt industries, organizations must prioritize reskilling and upskilling to remain competitive.

With these new skills, individuals can improve their job performance, take on new responsibilities, and advance their careers. Another benefit is organizations can prepare for the future, where new technologies and processes are likely to transform the way we work. By developing employees' skills in areas such as data analysis, automation, and AI, organizations can stay ahead of the curve and position themselves for success in the years to come.

Organizations that invest in their employees' professional growth not only improve employee retention and boost morale but also remain competitive in their respective industries. They should provide opportunities for training and development, offer mentorship and coaching programs, and promote a culture of continuous learning. By doing so, they can ensure that their employees have the necessary skills to adapt and thrive in a rapidly changing world.

One way to proactively address this is the work PwC is doing with UNICEF and the World Economic Forum to prepare youth for the future. The World Economic Forum launched the Reskilling Revolution initiative to train and futureproof one billion workers by 2030. Public-private partnerships like Luxembourg's Digital Skills Bridge project have been successful in helping train and retrain job seekers and current employees. Companies should also invest in developing their employees' soft skills that AI cannot replicate. Leveraging creativity, leadership, and emotional intelligence to create strong governance and organizational cultures to manage AI is critical. AI has the potential to create long-term job growth, but it is important to invest in high-quality education and upskilling opportunities to prepare society for this future.

In today's fast-paced world, technological advancements are rapidly changing the landscape of competition. The introduction of new technologies has created a leveling of the playing field, either by creating a more equitable distribution of resources and capabilities or by creating market dominance. Unfortunately, many large enterprises may not keep their employees current, which creates a vacuum for learning. To fill this gap, companies should allow side-hustles, which enable employees to develop new skills in their own time and on their own terms and bring this knowledge back to the office. This model benefits both the employee and the organization. This phenomenon drives individuals and organizations to strive to rise above the rest.

A modern-day Socratic method

AI also provides a scalable way to apply historically sound learning principles, like the Socratic Method. Developed by the Greek philosopher Socrates, this approach to learning is a dialogue between teacher and students. The conversation is encouraged by continual probing questions of the teacher, in a concerted effort to explore the underlying beliefs that shape the student's views and opinions.

Now, either in small groups or individual discussions, students can probe the teacher (AI) as part of a blended educational program. The meaningful answers the receive are the reward for learning how to ask the right questions or articulate the best prompts. This type of questioning is wonderful preparation for communicating with other humans as well. Through practice and experimentation, we can learn to be less ambiguous with how we collaborate and enable a level of clarity to get the results we desire. Fascinatingly enough, the AI is now capable of asking questions in return to help drive the dialog whereby a mutually acceptable solution is derived from the exchange.

In the late 1970s and early 1980s, good penmanship and long division were necessities for professional success. By the late 1980s, technology had rendered these skills obsolete. Education culture is slow to change, as evidenced by the fact that many schools still teach long division. According to John Villasenor, a professor at the University of California, Los Angeles, who is allowing students to use the AI chatbot ChatGPT in their writing assignments, "AI writing tools can help students learn to write better while also helping them achieve their goals outside of writing." AI tools should be used responsibly and with caution to ensure that students are not falsely accused of using them. Writing is an important skill that should be respected and taught properly.

Donald Clark, a well-known learning and development expert, calls this new educational domain "PedAIgogy." No longer are students relegated to ingesting knowledge with the hope that short term memory lasts long enough for the next test, and of course the dreaded end of year exams. With the addition of generative AI and natural language discussion, students are now able to apply knowledge in meaningful discourse, both with AI and each other.

The impact of prompt engineering and generative AI

The combination of prompt engineering and generative AI has the potential to level the playing field for individuals and organizations by providing access to an AI-powered server of knowledge and procedures. This would enable everyone in an organization to have essential information at their fingertips, with any new knowledge they generate automatically organized. This could result in greater collaboration and knowledge-sharing within organizations and make it easier for people to pursue their own interests and passions.

The use of these generative tools also provides immediate access to virtual assistants or agents that can write drafts, create software, provide feedback, and many other services that can upgrade the employee's capabilities without requiring months or years of training for proficiency. The new art of prompt engineering builds on Socratic skills that anyone can learn to master. Once they have that key, any number of skill locks can be opened and applied.

Education in the 21st century

In the 21st century, the collaboration of human educators and educational cobots will transform the learning landscape. Imagine cobots autonomously navigating classrooms, offering tailored assistance and real-time performance analysis to individual students, ensuring no one is left behind. They can also handle routine tasks, allowing educators to focus on teaching and strengthening the student-teacher bond.

Elementary

Education for children, especially early education through 8th grade, will benefit from some AI enhancement and EdTech tools for rote activities and safe discovery education activities. However, during these formative ages, the human interaction of teachers in the classroom is critical to the development of social skills, creative expression, personal coaching and mentoring, and conversational engagement. AI can assist in developing activities and performing repetitive administrative tasks freeing up valuable time for the teachers to spend more time with the children.

High school

Take for example the release of Khanmigo from Khan Academy. Over the past decade or more, Khan Academy has revolutionized the way students of all ages learn online. Now, with their newly released AI guide, they aim to provide one-on-one tutoring experiences customized for each student. This same assistant will be able to help teachers with administrative tasks.

Until now, one of the roadblocks for individualized learning plans for each student was the sheer time and effort required to adapt each lesson to diverse needs at scale. With AI, a teacher can now create one curriculum, one set of content, one set of assessments, and then as each student completes a personal preferences profile, AI can generate a variant that works for them. This is like the old concept of teaching percentages to a class full of students who struggle with math but can calculate the batting average of their favorite sports heroes. Only this time, it is scalable and from a context that works for each student.

Workforce training

On-the-job training requires a slightly different approach, but equally benefits from the power of AI. Sana Labs, a Learning Experience Platform developer, has created an AI powered system for knowledge sharing and automated administration to enable companies to "learn and perform 10x faster." According to their site, their platform is "powered by state-of-the art machine learning. Sana can generate polls, quizzes, automations, translations, and even entire courses for you." As this type of technology continues to grow, we will see training programs personalized for each employee to meet the changing requirements of the business and for their individual career paths.

Given that learning is not an event, but rather a journey, having a cobot partner will enable the continuous need for reskilling and upskilling. Cobots are extremely versatile and adaptable machines equipped with advanced sensors, AI algorithms, and safety features that enable them to learn from and interact with their human counterparts in real-time. They can quickly adapt to new tasks and refine their skills over time. This mutual learning process paves the way for a future in which humans and robots work in harmony, each leveraging their respective strengths to drive innovation and efficiency in the workplace.

In the Netflix documentary, "The Social Dilemma" (a must watch for everyone) I realized what they were describing was not just the impact of social media and social networks on our society. They were describing a fundamental change in how we might consider training or behavioral modification in the future. They describe the process of their AI networking systems gathering immense amounts of data about each of us and then use that data to formulate a prescription to train us to stay engaged with their systems, their advertisers, and their messaging. The outcome of being a part of the system is modifying our behavior for shopping, voting, organizing our communities, etc. This process occurs in micro-increments over weeks and months. Imagine if we could apply these same techniques for good. We can develop a desire for learning, being better managers and employees, supporting our communities through corporate outreach, and becoming better at our jobs. While AI is the underlying engine to influence you and I, it is also capable of improving education and the lives of us all.

Natural language processing (NLP) and generative AI
Machine learning is transforming education by enabling more personalized, adaptive, and accessible learning experiences, automating assessments and grading, and providing new tools and resources to support both children and adult learners. These technologies have the potential to significantly improve educational outcomes and to make education more inclusive and accessible to a diverse range of learners.

Personalized learning
Machine learning algorithms can analyze individual learner data, such as performance, learning style, and preferences, in order to provide personalized content, feedback, and recommendations. This helps create a tailored learning experience that caters to each learner's unique needs and fosters better engagement and outcomes.

Adaptive learning systems

Machine learning can be employed to develop adaptive learning systems that dynamically adjust the difficulty and pace of instructional content based on the learner's progress and performance. This helps maintain an appropriate level of challenge and keeps learners motivated and engaged.

Intelligent tutoring systems

NLP and machine learning can be used to create AI-powered tutors that provide instant feedback, hints, and explanations to learners, simulating the experience of one-on-one tutoring and enhancing the learning process.

Automatic assessment and grading

NLP and machine learning algorithms can be used to automatically assess and grade learner submissions, such as essays, short answers, and even code. This can save educators time and provide learners with immediate feedback, allowing them to learn from their mistakes and improve more quickly.

Language translation and support

NLP can facilitate the automatic translation of educational content, making it accessible to a broader audience of learners who speak different languages. In addition, NLP can be used to create tools that provide real-time language support, such as grammar and pronunciation assistance.

Learning analytics

Machine learning can analyze data from various sources, such as learner interactions, assessments, and other activities, to provide insights into learning patterns and outcomes. These insights can inform educators and institutions on how to improve instructional design, content delivery, and learner support.

Gamification and simulation

Generative AI and machine learning can be employed to create engaging, interactive educational experiences, such as games and simulations that adapt to learners' abilities and progress.

Accessibility and inclusivity

NLP and machine learning can help create educational tools and platforms that are more accessible to learners with disabilities, such as text-to-speech, speech-to-text, and automatic image captioning.

Knowledge discovery and organization

NLP can be used to analyze vast amounts of textual data, such as research articles, books, and online resources, to identify relevant information, summarize content, and organize knowledge in a more accessible and intuitive manner.

Educational chatbots and virtual assistants

AI-powered chatbots and virtual assistants can answer questions, provide guidance, and support learners throughout their educational journey, making it easier for them to access the information they need.

The synergy of human educators and educational automation promises to revolutionize the way knowledge is acquired and shared. This innovative approach to education prepares students for an interconnected world while instilling solid inquiry-based learning skills.

All of this can potentially lead us to a more discovery-based approach to learning and training. If visual and audio recognition is added to the data inputs, the Socratic push from the AI can even be proactive. Imagine if, while performing a task, an employee is asked by the AI, "why are you doing that?" Based on the response, the AI may provide guidance or ask additional questions to help it provide feedback to improve the employee performance.

Action Items

1. Implement employee engagement surveys to detect and address the root cause of quiet quitting.
2. Provide opportunities for employee upskilling and reskilling to adapt to technological advancements and changes in the workforce.
3. Develop a culture of continuous learning by promoting mentorship and coaching programs, and providing training and development opportunities.
4. Invest in developing soft skills such as creativity, leadership, and emotional intelligence, that AI cannot replicate.

5. Allow and encourage side-hustles to enable employees to develop new skills and bring knowledge back to the organization.
6. Develop prompt engineering skills to leverage generative AI and make knowledge more accessible and organized within organizations.
7. Embrace both adaptation and adoption strategies to manage change effectively and remain competitive in the modern workplace.
8. Invest in educational cobots to augment human educators and enable tailored assistance and real-time performance analysis to individual students, while handling routine tasks.
9. Provide continuous reskilling and upskilling opportunities to employees to keep up with the rapidly changing job market, leveraging the versatility and adaptability of cobots to enable a journey-based approach to learning.
10. Develop adaptive learning systems that dynamically adjust the difficulty and pace of instructional content based on the learner's progress and performance, maintaining an appropriate level of challenge and keeping learners motivated and engaged.
11. Create AI-powered tutors that provide instant feedback, hints, and explanations to learners, simulating the experience of one-on-one tutoring and enhancing the learning process.
12. Use NLP and machine learning algorithms to automatically assess and grade learner submissions, such as essays, short answers, and even code, saving educators time, and providing learners with immediate feedback.
13. Employ NLP to facilitate the automatic translation of educational content, making it accessible to a broader audience of learners who may

speak different languages, and to create tools that provide real-time language support, such as grammar and pronunciation assistance.

14. Employ generative AI and machine learning to create engaging, interactive educational experiences, such as games and simulations that adapt to learners' abilities and progress, fostering better engagement and outcomes.

15. Use NLP and machine learning to create educational tools and platforms that are more accessible to learners with disabilities, such as text-to-speech, speech-to-text, and automatic image captioning.

Chapter 8: There is AI in TEAM

Teams have been an integral part of human society since the dawn of time. From hunting parties to sports teams and business teams, we have relied on the strengths and abilities of our teammates to achieve success. Now, with the introduction of advanced technology, the definition of team is evolving rapidly. The inclusion of transhuman and non-human team members, such as advanced robotics and AI, is changing the dynamics of team performance and challenging traditional team structures.

"I believe the future of AI is actually interdependence, collaboration, and cooperation between people and systems, both at the macro [and micro] levels," said Justine Cassell, founding member, Paris AI Research Institute, and faculty member of the Human-Computer Interaction Institute at Carnegie Mellon University.

"At the macro-level, [look], for example, at robots on the factory floor," she said. "Today, there's been a lot of fear about how autonomous they actually are. First of all, they're often dangerous. They're so autonomous, you have to get out of their way. And it would be nice if they were more interdependent. If we could be there at the same time as they are."

Advanced robotics and AI are complementing and working alongside human team members in various capacities in many businesses today and potentially all organizations in the next few years. These new "employees" are not just relegated to the factory floor either. They are now in offices and boardrooms impacting business decisions at all levels of their organizations. The introduction of this technology is not a question of "if" business functions are changing, but rather "when" we will catch up with the changes that are already here and

114

continue multiplying exponentially. Enterprises larger than 1000 employees face a particularly difficult challenge. Due to the scale of change, technology implementation costs, reaction time, risk, and other factors, can make pivoting in today's talent market very difficult.

The Rise of Transhuman and Non-Human Team Members

As we have covered, the integration of advanced technology in teams has given rise to a new generation of transhumans who can possess superhuman strength, endurance, and resilience beyond what is traditionally considered human. Conditions previously thought of as disabilities are now advantages in certain sports and industries through the application of state-of-the-art prosthetics. This evolution has inspired activity across the globe to develop advanced robotics and AI that can be integrated into teams of all types in order to complement and compensate for gaps in human performance, skills, and physical capabilities.

The inclusion of AI in teams is changing traditional team structures in different organizations. AI can analyze vast amounts of data and supply insights that were previously impossible to obtain. This has made it possible to create teams that are more diverse and inclusive. AI can help identify team members with complementary skills, enabling organizations to create teams that are better equipped to handle complex tasks.

The introduction of AI in teams also presents challenges. AI cannot replace human creativity, intuition, and empathy, which are essential human qualities that cannot be replicated by machines. AI may be able to create images, text, video, and other "artistic" or "creative" content, but they are dependent on humans to provide the catalyst or prompt or question that drives the machine to produce those products. Machines are for all practical purpose intelligent tools. And, like a shovel does not dig unless a human provides a reason, neither does AI spontaneously create without a human providing inspiration. Organizations must strike a balance between human and AI capabilities to create high-performing teams.

Thanks to books and movies, our traditional image of AI ranges from humanoid to a sliding puck sucking up dust from our floors. And let's not forget the ever-vigilant coffee tabletop cylinders that listen for our requests for music or paper towels. The interesting thing about AI, however, is it is not limited to any specific form. In fact, if you consider "the cloud" as its native state, AI is formless. A stream of algorithms spread across multiple servers connected to a myriad of data sources, both hardware and software. But for some reason, we want AI to resemble us most of all.

When I was in industrial design school a few decades ago, I had a professor, Dr. Michael Pause, who banned me from the machine shop for one semester. Apparently, I was limiting my designs to what I could build, not what I could dream. He said I should be forcing new tools and processes to be created because of my designs instead of the other way around. I think that is where we are with AI and robotics today. There are a few outliers, but in most cases, we are confining our creativity to a narrow perception of what robots should be instead of what they can be.

The same goes for human augmentation. We have finally reached the point where we can replace a damaged or missing limb with an artificial one. In some situations, the new limb is more stylish or capable than the real one it replaced.

In the end though, the replacement is just that - a replacement. Now, imagine if we deliberately made the new limb better than the original. It could be fireproof. It could be stronger. It could be like a tentacle. It could have interchangeable attachments. It might not look or function like the original at all. Once the possibility is acknowledged, a whole spectrum of capabilities can be imagined.

As humans, we look for characteristics that conform us to look the same, function the same, be the same. That's why during our rebellious phases, many of us try to find ways to be unique - purple hair, body piercing, tattoos, etc. For most, that is as far as they go. Occasionally someone will go out on a limb and do something drastic and embed an IoT device or deliberately disfigure their bodies. Our cobots are in the same boat (just not rebellious yet). We are forcing them to be human-like to their own detriment. Why should a cobot have to walk (a rather limiting feature) or have arms that pivot with the same restrictions as human arms?

To take advantage of how AI and robots can improve our businesses, you must first recognize this is not an either-or situation. In fact, according to a study of thousands of companies shared by Shervin Khodabandeh on a TED Talk, "Only about 10 percent of these companies get any meaningful financial impact from their investments [in AI]. These 10 percent winners with AI have a secret. And their secret is not about fancy algorithms or sophisticated technology. It's something far more basic. It's how they get their people and AI to work together. Together, not against each other, not instead of each other. Together in a mutually beneficial relationship."

Humanity is at a turning point. Social acceptance is undergoing immense pressures for all categories of diversity and inclusion. We need to recognize that the question facing us is more than the 160+ measurements of diversity. The question now is will we truly accept those who are different if those differences make them more capable, more intelligent, more powerful than the rest of us?

Business teams

The inclusion of these new team members has a significant impact on human business teams. Cobots can be used to automate repetitive tasks, such as assembly, data entry, and processing. This will free up human team members to focus on strategic and creative tasks. Transhumans can work in ways normal humans cannot. From hazardous conditions to physically challenging tasks to data recall, they can add significant capability to many operations. This change can help organizations reduce costs and increase efficiency.

One way companies can achieve true teamwork through adding technology to their workforce is by teaching human employees how to work with conversational AI and generative AI and not just see them as tools. By including AI in business conversations, companies will increase their research capabilities. Conducting a dialog with conversational AI produces better results than single commands. Using AI to help ideate through and generate new ideas can breakdown "white canvas syndrome" or the times where "writer's block" or the silent room is preventing the human employees from applying their creativity. Generative AI for visuals is similar, and because it often creates abstract designs, it can help tear down mental barriers and lead to new ideas by looking at things from a different point of view.

Another area seeing a huge resurgence is performance support. With modern digital adoption platforms, performance support can be integrated into agile tools employees use daily. These platforms evolve as they interact with your employees, and as a result, performance support evolves with it. These tools can be used for onboarding new employees, and in some cases automate entire processes, thus reducing employee task time and improving efficiency. Best of all, these frameworks can identify employees requiring a personal touch and link them to formal learning or live subject matter experts at the time of need.

Organization in-house experts are now able to focus on performing the roles they were hired to do. The workforce can be more productive, because skill gaps can be identified and corrected without embarrassment or added delays due to an expert sidelined to help a peer. Teams across an organization will be able to have a shared standard way of operating that is continuously monitored and improved. Proactive automated feedback will help drive competence, confidence, and consistency across your entire organization.

Virtual teams

For over fifty years, companies have been outsourcing more and more of their business to labor forces in other countries. From the garment industry, to contact centers, to data collection and analysis, to software programming, not to mention all of the manufacturing of parts or complete finished goods, we have seen the shift of production. More recently, this outsourcing has become virtual insourcing, as remote employees around the globe work together but in different locations. Some of this is due to cost, some due to scale and availability of resources, and some due to around-the-clock schedules. AI and cobots are simply the newest members of the virtual team.

These digital assistants enable small human teams to compete with larger traditional teams to design, produce, and deliver a wide array of products and services. A single programmer can have a team of AI assistants helping to code apps in days that used to take months, even in languages or with frameworks they are not as experienced in using. A single marketing person can produce hundreds of blogs, posts, emails, and other communications by asking the right questions of their AI ghost writers and automated distribution managers. A small farmer can manage a huge farm, operating 24 hours a day, by using automated equipment and soil, weed, and crop maintenance AI.

This is not about replacing humans. This is about empowering small businesses to compete at a local and global level to meet the demands now and in the future.

Sports teams

Sports teams are also being impacted by the inclusion of advanced technologies. Wearable technology, such as smartwatches and fitness trackers, can be used to monitor players' performance and health, helping coaches make better decisions about player training and game strategy. Exoskeletons and other advanced technologies can be used to enhance players' strength, endurance, and agility, giving teams a competitive advantage.

Game analytics ranging from full field tracking to strike zone monitoring are changing the nature of coaching and feedback as well. Even sports as wide-ranging as golf and Formula One racing are benefiting from AI connectivity to internet of things (IoT) data sources and biometric devices. The analytics not only support performance feedback, but also can anticipate potential health concerns and player conditions before, during and after their activities. All this data leads to safer sporting events and better results for the individual and the team.

Government and corporate leadership teams

The introduction of advanced technologies is also impacting government and political teams. AI can be used to analyze vast amounts of data and provide insights that can help policymakers make better decisions. For example, AI can be used to analyze economic data to find trends and inform fiscal policy decisions. Boards of directors of major corporations are also being impacted by the introduction of AI. AI can be used to analyze company data and provide insights that can help boards make better decisions, such as analyzing financial data to identify trends and inform investments.

As organizations continue to adapt to the changes brought about by the inclusion of all types of employees, the role of leadership will also need to evolve. Leaders must understand the capabilities and limitations of AI and robotics and determine how best to integrate these technologies into their teams to achieve optimal performance.

Building on each other's strengths

In order to prepare for upcoming changes, companies should perform a thorough evaluation of themselves. According to Ali Raza, founder and CEO of ThroughPut, an operations AI company, the focus of automation strategy should not be on when to automate, but rather on where to automate. The first step is to streamline processes and bring them under control, which makes them easier to scale. Hugh Dyar, senior vice-president of marketing for Sapience Analytics, suggests that businesses should consider the value and cost of tasks before adopting process automation. They should examine their workflow to identify labor-intensive processes and determine which parts of those processes drive the most cost.

Here are some examples of various industries and how the partnership of humans, augmented humans, and non-humans can help organizations be competitive now and in the future. The amount of impact will depend on the nature of the work - some tasks are still too difficult for machines to do cost effectively or at all - and the approach, whether complete replacement or simply enhancing the human capabilities.

The new legal team

Generative AI has the potential to transform the legal profession:

Legal research
AI can quickly and efficiently analyze large amounts of legal documents, case law, and legislation to help lawyers identify relevant information and precedents.

Contract review and analysis
AI can review contracts, identify inconsistencies, errors, and potential risks, and suggest improvements or modifications.

Document drafting

AI can generate standard legal documents, such as contracts, wills, and agreements, based on user input and templates, saving time, and reducing errors.

Litigation prediction

AI can analyze historical case data to predict the outcome of ongoing cases, enabling lawyers to make more informed decisions on case strategies.

E-discovery

AI can quickly review and categorize large volumes of electronic documents during the discovery phase of litigation, improving efficiency and accuracy.

Intellectual property analysis

AI can analyze patents, trademarks, and copyrights to help with intellectual property (IP) protection and infringement identification.

Regulatory compliance

AI can monitor and analyze changes in regulations to help organizations stay compliant with relevant laws.

Legal roles likely to be replaced or significantly impacted by AI include:

Paralegals and legal assistants

Many of their tasks, such as legal research, document preparation, and organization, can be automated through AI.

Document reviewers

AI can efficiently review and categorize large volumes of documents, which may reduce the demand for human document reviewers.

Junior associates

AI may take over some of the tasks typically assigned to junior lawyers, such as legal research, contract review, and document drafting.

New legal roles anticipated as a result of AI and robotics include:

Legal technologists

Humans who understand both law and technology, and can develop, implement, and maintain AI and other tech solutions in legal practice.

AI ethics and regulation specialists

They will focus on AI ethics and regulatory compliance to help organizations navigate the legal and ethical implications of AI usage.

Legal data scientists

Individuals who specialize in analyzing large volumes of legal data, using AI and other data analytics tools to provide insights and support decision-making.

AI trainers and educators

Individuals responsible for training AI systems in the legal context and educating legal professionals on how to use AI tools effectively.

Legal innovation consultants

Consultants who help law firms and legal departments develop strategies for incorporating AI and other technological innovations into their practice.

While AI has the potential to replace or augment certain roles in the legal profession, it is also likely to create new opportunities and demand for legal professionals with expertise in AI, data analysis, and technology.

Not business as usual

Cobots are revolutionizing various aspects of finance and business management, including risk management, investment, customer service, and more. Here's how these technologies are impacting the industry:

Risk management and fraud detection

Machine learning algorithms can analyze large datasets to identify patterns and anomalies, helping financial institutions detect and prevent fraudulent activities, assess credit risk, and monitor compliance with regulations.

Algorithmic trading

Machine learning models can analyze historical and real-time market data to identify trends and generate trading signals, enabling more efficient and profitable trading strategies.

Portfolio management and investment advice

Machine learning and generative AI can help financial advisors and investors make better-informed decisions by analyzing market trends, assessing risk, and optimizing portfolio allocation based on individual goals and preferences.

Financial forecasting

NLP and machine learning can be used to analyze data from various sources, such as financial reports, news articles, and social media, to predict market trends, stock prices, and economic indicators, enabling more accurate forecasting and informed decision-making.

Customer service and support

AI-powered chatbots and virtual assistants can handle customer inquiries, provide personalized financial advice, and assist with transactions, improving customer satisfaction and reducing response times.

Process automation

Machine learning and NLP can automate various tasks in finance and business management, such as data entry, invoice processing, and reconciliation, leading to increased efficiency and reduced costs.

Sentiment analysis

NLP can analyze text data from sources like news articles, financial reports, and social media to gauge market sentiment and predict its impact on asset prices.

Document analysis and extraction

NLP can be used to analyze and extract relevant information from unstructured documents, such as contracts, regulatory filings, and financial statements, streamlining due diligence and compliance processes.

Financial planning and budgeting

Machine learning and generative AI can help businesses analyze historical financial data, identify trends, and develop more accurate budgets and forecasts.

Human resources and talent management

NLP and machine learning can be employed to analyze job applications, employee performance data, and other sources to improve hiring decisions, identify top talent, and optimize workforce management.

Partners in manufacturing

The story of an automotive factory serves as a case study in the power of cobots to revolutionize the manufacturing sector. Here, cobots work alongside human technicians, performing tasks such as precision welding, assembly, and quality control. By sharing the workload and complementing one another's strengths, the human-cobot team achieves unprecedented levels of efficiency and productivity in many ways:

Predictive maintenance

Machine learning algorithms can analyze data from sensors and historical maintenance records to predict when equipment is likely to fail or require maintenance. This helps manufacturers optimize maintenance schedules, reduce downtime, and improve overall equipment efficiency.

Quality control and defect detection

Machine learning models can be trained to analyze images, videos, and other data from production lines to detect defects, irregularities, or deviations from set standards. This allows manufacturers to identify issues in real-time, reduce waste, and maintain high-quality standards.

Production optimization

Machine learning can be used to optimize production processes by analyzing data from multiple sources, such as sensors, equipment, and production schedules. This enables manufacturers to identify bottlenecks, improve resource allocation, and adjust production to maximize efficiency.

Supply chain management

NLP and machine learning can analyze data from various sources, including supplier information, market trends, and consumer demand, to optimize supply chain operations. This can help manufacturers reduce costs, minimize stockouts, and improve overall supply chain performance.

Design and prototyping

Generative AI can assist in the design process by generating new product concepts or optimizing existing designs based on specific constraints and requirements. This can help manufacturers reduce time-to-market and improve product quality.

Human-robot collaboration

NLP enables more natural and intuitive interaction between humans and robots on the factory floor, allowing for smoother collaboration and increased productivity. This can also improve worker safety by enabling robots to understand and respond to voice commands or other forms of input.

Training and knowledge transfer

NLP and generative AI can be employed to create adaptive, interactive learning platforms for training workers in new skills or updating their knowledge on the latest manufacturing technologies and best practices.

Decision support systems

Integrating NLP, generative AI, and machine learning into decision support systems can help manufacturers make more informed decisions by providing real-time insights, predictions, and recommendations based on their specific context.

Customer support and service

AI-powered chatbots and virtual assistants can handle customer inquiries, provide technical support, and assist with product troubleshooting, reducing response times and improving customer satisfaction.

Market analysis and forecasting

NLP and machine learning can be used to analyze market trends, competitor activities, and consumer sentiment, helping manufacturers make strategic decisions related to product development, marketing, and pricing.

The new healthcare team

In a state-of-the-art hospital, a surgeon and a robotic assistant collaborate on a complex and delicate procedure. The cobot, equipped with AI-powered image recognition and advanced surgical tools, provides crucial support and guidance to the surgeon, enhancing the precision and safety of the operation. This collaborative partnership exemplifies the transformative potential of cobots in healthcare, where they can help to save lives, reduce human error, and improve patient outcomes.

Healthcare is one of the sectors where natural language processing (NLP), generative AI, and machine learning have made significant inroads, leading to improvements in various aspects of patient care, diagnostics, and research. Here's how these technologies are impacting healthcare:

Medical diagnosis

Machine learning algorithms can analyze medical images (e.g., X-rays, MRIs, and CT scans) to identify patterns and detect diseases or abnormalities more accurately and faster than human experts. This can help improve diagnostic accuracy, reduce the time to treatment, and potentially save lives.

Personalized medicine

Machine learning can analyze large datasets of patient information, genetic data, and clinical outcomes to identify patterns and relationships, allowing for the development of more targeted and personalized treatment plans.

Drug discovery

Generative AI can help expedite the drug discovery process by generating novel molecular structures, predicting their properties, and identifying potential drug candidates. This can significantly reduce the time and cost associated with traditional drug discovery methods.

Electronic health records (EHRs)

NLP can be used to analyze unstructured data in EHRs, such as clinical notes, to extract meaningful information, identify trends, and provide insights for better patient care.

Clinical decision support

NLP and machine learning can be integrated into clinical decision support systems to provide real-time recommendations and insights to healthcare professionals based on patient data, medical guidelines, and research findings.

Disease outbreak prediction and surveillance

Machine learning models can analyze data from various sources, such as social media, news, and travel records, to predict and monitor disease outbreaks, helping public health officials respond more effectively to emerging threats.

Chatbots and virtual assistants

AI-powered chatbots and virtual assistants can provide medical information, answer questions, and help triage patient symptoms, improving access to healthcare services and reducing the workload on healthcare professionals.

Telemedicine

Machine learning and NLP can enhance telemedicine platforms by providing real-time transcription of patient-provider interactions, language translation, and remote monitoring of patients' vital signs.

Healthcare administration

AI and machine learning can optimize hospital workflows, patient scheduling, and resource allocation, leading to more efficient healthcare operations and reduced costs.

Medical research

NLP can be used to analyze vast amounts of scientific literature, identify trends, and generate hypotheses, accelerating the pace of medical research and discovery.

Natural language processing, generative AI, and machine learning are playing a crucial role in transforming the healthcare industry by improving diagnostics, enhancing patient care, personalizing treatments, and streamlining administrative tasks, ultimately leading to better health outcomes and reduced costs.

Cobots in agriculture

On a sprawling, sun-drenched farm, a team of human workers and agricultural cobots join forces to plant, cultivate, and harvest crops. The cobots, equipped with AI-driven navigation systems and an array of sensors, autonomously traverse the fields, performing tasks such as soil analysis, planting seeds, and monitoring crop health. By working together, the human-cobot team can dramatically increase agricultural yields, reduce waste, and optimize resource usage, all while minimizing the environmental impact of farming.

Farming is an industry that has been continuously evolving with advancements in technology, and natural language processing (NLP), generative AI, and machine learning are playing a significant role in shaping its future. Here are some ways these technologies impact farming:

Precision agriculture: NLP and machine learning algorithms can analyze vast amounts of data from different sources such as satellite imagery, weather data, and soil sensors to provide farmers with real-time insights and recommendations on optimizing farm management. This can help improve crop yields, reduce costs, and minimize the environmental impact.

Crop monitoring and disease detection

Machine learning models can be trained to identify patterns in images, helping to detect early signs of crop diseases, pests, or nutrient deficiencies. Farmers can then take preventive measures to minimize crop loss and maintain optimal crop health.

Automated machinery

NLP and machine learning are essential components in developing autonomous farming equipment, such as self-driving tractors and harvesters. These technologies enable the machinery to process and respond to voice commands or other types of input, which improves efficiency and reduces the need for manual labor.

Decision support systems

By integrating NLP, generative AI, and machine learning into decision support systems, farmers can receive customized advice based on their specific needs and context. This can include recommendations on crop selection, planting times, irrigation schedules, and pest control strategies.

Market analysis and forecasting

Advanced algorithms can analyze market trends and predict future demand for various crops, helping farmers make informed decisions about which crops to grow and when to sell their produce to maximize profits.

Knowledge sharing and collaboration

NLP can facilitate the exchange of information among farmers by automatically translating content between different languages and analyzing textual data from various sources such as research articles, news, and social media. This can help farmers stay updated on the latest farming techniques, innovations, and best practices.

Chatbots and virtual assistants

Farmers can use AI-powered chatbots and virtual assistants to answer questions, provide guidance, and even help diagnose crop issues. These tools can save time and make it easier for farmers to access the information they need.

Education and training

NLP and generative AI can be employed to create interactive, adaptive learning platforms tailored to individual needs, helping to train the next generation of farmers in modern agricultural practices and technologies.

Overall, natural language processing, generative AI, and machine learning are transforming the farming industry by enabling better decision-making, improving efficiency, reducing costs, and promoting more sustainable and environmentally friendly practices.

Revolutionizing shipping and transportation

Cobots are not simply about replicating humans in the workplace. They include any number of types of robots from warehouse stock and retrieve to fully autonomous trucks and ships. These technologies are revolutionizing various aspects of transportation, including vehicle autonomy, traffic management, and logistics. Here's a few ways these technologies are impacting the transportation industry:

Autonomous vehicles

Machine learning and computer vision technologies play a crucial role in developing self-driving vehicles. These algorithms can process large amounts of data from sensors, cameras, and other sources in real-time to make driving decisions, improving safety and efficiency on the road.

Traffic management

Machine learning models can analyze data from various sources, such as traffic cameras, sensors, and historical patterns, to optimize traffic signal timings, predict congestion, and suggest alternative routes. This can help reduce travel times, emissions, and overall traffic congestion.

Public transportation

NLP and machine learning can be used to optimize public transportation schedules, predict maintenance needs, and analyze passenger data to improve overall service and efficiency.

Logistics and supply chain optimization

Machine learning can help optimize routing and scheduling for delivery trucks, reducing fuel consumption, travel time, and costs. Additionally, NLP and machine learning can be used to forecast demand, manage inventory, and improve overall supply chain efficiency.

Vehicle maintenance and diagnostics

Predictive maintenance algorithms can analyze data from vehicle sensors to identify potential issues before they become critical, reducing maintenance costs and downtime.

Customer support and interaction

AI-powered chatbots and virtual assistants can handle customer inquiries, provide real-time travel updates, and assist with booking and ticketing, improving the overall customer experience.

Safety and security

Machine learning and computer vision can be employed to monitor transportation infrastructure, such as bridges and tunnels, to detect potential safety hazards or security breaches.

Urban planning and infrastructure development

Generative AI and machine learning can help analyze large datasets, such as traffic patterns and demographic information, to inform the design and development of transportation infrastructure projects.

Environmental impact assessment

Machine learning models can analyze data related to emissions, traffic patterns, and fuel consumption to help transportation authorities make more informed decisions regarding environmental policies and regulations.

Human-machine interaction

NLP can facilitate more natural interaction between humans and transportation systems, enabling voice-activated controls, real-time translation services, and other forms of intuitive communication.

Augmenting law enforcement

Human augmentation, cobots, and AI are likely to have a significant impact on law enforcement in the coming years. Here are a few potential ways that these technologies could be used:

Human augmentation

Law enforcement officers could use wearable technology to enhance their physical abilities, such as exoskeletons that increase strength and endurance. This could help officers perform their duties more effectively and safely.

Cobots

Collaborative robots, or cobots, could be used to assist law enforcement officers in a variety of tasks, such as bomb disposal or search and rescue operations. Cobots could also be used to perform dangerous tasks that would otherwise put officers at risk.

Artificial Intelligence

AI could be used to analyze large amounts of data to help law enforcement agencies identify patterns and predict criminal activity. AI could also be used to automate routine tasks, such as paperwork and data entry, freeing up officers to focus on more important tasks.

Operations

Human augmentation and cobots could be used to assist law enforcement officers in a variety of tasks, such as bomb disposal, search and rescue operations, and crowd control. AI could be used to analyze large amounts of data to help law enforcement agencies identify patterns and predict criminal activity.

Training

Human augmentation could be used to enhance the physical abilities of law enforcement officers, such as strength and endurance. AI could be used to provide virtual training simulations that help officers develop their skills and improve their decision-making abilities.

Investigations

AI could be used to analyze large amounts of data to help detectives identify suspects and solve crimes. Cobots could be used to perform dangerous tasks, such as collecting evidence from crime scenes.

Court proceedings

AI could be used to analyze legal documents and assist court officials in making decisions. AI could also be used to provide virtual courtrooms that allow witnesses to testify remotely.

Police officers may need to be trained to use new technologies, such as exoskeletons or cobots. Detectives may need to learn how to use AI tools to analyze data and solve crimes. Court officials may need to adapt to new technologies that change the way court proceedings are conducted.

Overall, these technologies have the potential to make law enforcement more effective and efficient, but they also raise important ethical and privacy concerns that must be addressed. It will be important for law enforcement agencies to carefully consider the implications of these technologies and ensure that they are used in a responsible and ethical manner.

Transhuman resources

In this new environment, leaders must evolve their HR practices by investing in algorithms that can identify worker skills and competencies and modify worker profile tools to display examples of work rather than job titles. When recruiting algorithms incorporate AI to determine whether to hire someone, it is essential to ensure that bias is removed from the equation. This means not including photos of job candidates and removing references to race, culture, mental or physical challenges, or where any other diversity components come into play. The same goes for residential addresses and other non-essential background information. The entire recruiting process needs to be re-evaluated for the 21st-century workplace. In order to include everyone, we need to update people management to include the machines.

Inclusivity means everyone

However, ensuring inclusivity in the workplace does not end with the recruitment process. Humans are social creatures and tend to flock to those like themselves, leading to social groupings that lack diversity. In a world without boundaries, we will invent our own, and it is up to businesses to actively create an area of mutual interest and construct specific business-oriented boundaries to provide environments for diverse teams to foster successful innovation.

Transhumanist behavior is, by nature, inclusive, which means that businesses need to gather a diverse mix of human and non-human team members and actively take steps to align their strategies by involving all parts of the organization. Successful organizations see the competitive advantage of inclusivity and the benefit of multiple minds.

141

Talent disruption is at hand. The rise of the human, augmented human, and non-human workforce presents new challenges for those in talent management. Traditional HR practices will need to evolve to include resources that are innately transhuman or not human at all. Over the centuries, companies have had to adjust these same policies for the marginalized and the physically challenged. Companies may need to reevaluate the way they hire and train both in recruiting and the daily work of each employee to ensure that they accommodate people with advanced abilities and incorporate them into their teams effectively. Organizations need to consider the entire employee and team dynamic and prepare and execute a shift from traditional Human Resources to Transhuman Resources to help navigate these new waters.

Furthermore, leaders must also consider the ethical implications of these technologies. The integration of AI and robotics in teams raises questions about the future of work and the role of humans in the workforce. Will these technologies create a more equitable and inclusive workforce, or will they further widen the gap between the haves and the have-nots? Leaders must navigate these complex ethical questions and ensure that the adoption of these technologies aligns with their organization's values.

Recruiting the best candidates

One of the key challenges facing talent management is identifying and recruiting the right talent for the job. With the introduction of AI and robotics, traditional job roles are changing, and new roles are emerging. Studies have shown cobots can reduce risk and improve productivity. Cobots are designed to work alongside humans and can take on dangerous or physically demanding tasks, reducing the risk of injury to human workers. This can help organizations improve workplace safety and reduce workers' compensation costs. An unintended consequence of this is that AI and natural language processing are making candidate evaluation even more complicated.

Imagine for a moment you are considering two candidates, A and B, for a financial risk assessment position in your company. One is well studied and has memorized all of the regulatory statutes and can recall the formulas for every calculation required to do their job. The other understands the need for the regulatory statutes and knows where to find the information. And, while they cannot recall from memory all of the formulas, they do know the right questions to ask if someone else can do the math. The latter candidate also knows how to use the latest NLP technology and through effective prompting, can have their AI powered "assistant" find the answers and perform the calculations when asked. In fact, because they have not memorized the materials, but rather learned how to partner to get the results they need based on the latest information, their application of what they find may be superior to their knowledgeable peer.

Recruitment and talent development will need to consider not only what employees know, but how well they can partner with technology to improve efficiency, accuracy, and application. New skills in creative problem solving and collaboration will be just as important as academic credentials. We will need to train both talent management and the institutions that are preparing people for the modern workforce in how these changes may impact their ability to be hired and grow in an organization.

As the world becomes increasingly diverse in terms of gender, ethnicity, culture, religion, sexual identification, and ideas, the need for inclusivity in the workplace has never been more pressing. The emergence of transhumanism, which has the potential to allow us to be whatever we want physically or virtually, presents both opportunities and challenges for businesses.

When using AI, ethical and legal implications should also be considered. One significant challenge in ensuring inclusivity is the potential for AI to perpetuate bias. AI systems can be biased if trained on biased data, which can lead to discriminatory outcomes and perpetuate existing inequalities. AI algorithms are only as objective as the data they are trained on, and if the data reflects the biases of society, the AI will learn those biases and perpetuate them. This issue has been particularly evident in the recruitment process, where AI algorithms have been found to discriminate against candidates based on gender, ethnicity, and other factors.

To combat this, AI should be blind to characteristics such as race, gender, and age. Recruitment algorithms should focus solely on a candidate's qualifications, skills, and experience, rather than any characteristics that could be used to discriminate against them or provide preferential treatment (Ivy League versus Community College for example). Additionally, businesses need to actively monitor their AI algorithms to ensure that they are not perpetuating bias and adjust them accordingly.

To remove bias from recruitment algorithms, businesses must take a data-driven approach to recruitment. This might involve analyzing recruitment data to identify patterns of bias and taking steps to address those biases. It might also involve partnering with organizations that specialize in diversity and inclusion to ensure that recruitment practices are inclusive and free from bias.

Moreover, AI should not only be blind to characteristics that could be used to discriminate against candidates but also actively work to promote inclusivity. For example, AI algorithms could be used to identify and highlight job openings to candidates from underrepresented groups, and offer training and support to help them succeed in the workplace.

Explainable AI

To ensure that AI is used effectively and ethically in the recruitment process, businesses need to develop clear guidelines and policies for its use. These guidelines should be based on ethical principles such as fairness, transparency, and accountability, and should be regularly reviewed and updated to reflect changing societal norms and values.

It is important to ensure that AI systems are designed and implemented in an ethical manner, with proper oversight and accountability mechanisms in place. This is especially relevant when applied to recruiting and hiring practices. One way to ensure ethical AI is using explainable AI (XAI). XAI is a branch of AI that aims to make the decision-making processes of AI systems transparent and understandable to humans. By providing explanations for how an AI system arrived at a particular decision or recommendation, XAI can help build trust and ensure that AI is being used in an ethical and responsible manner.

Thus, it is imperative to ensure that AI algorithms are developed without any bias, and that they are not influenced by any discriminatory factors such as race, ethnicity, culture, religion, gender, or sexual orientation. This means that the recruiting process needs to be reevaluated for the current and future workplace, and HR leaders must invest in algorithms that identify worker skills and competencies.

AI blindness is not just about removing bias; it is also about creating an environment in which everyone feels comfortable and included. To achieve this, businesses must adopt a culture of openness and transparency, where everyone is encouraged to share their ideas and opinions. This requires leaders to be more than just managers; they must be coaches and mentors, inspiring their teams to be creative, innovative, and inclusive.

Action Items

1. Identify skill gaps in your organization and assess the potential of transhuman and non-human team members.
2. Evaluate costs and benefits of implementing advanced robotics and AI in your teams.
3. Implement cobots to automate repetitive tasks and allow human team members to focus on higher-level tasks.
4. Explore wearable technology and exoskeletons to enhance team performance and gain a competitive advantage.
5. Develop an understanding of AI and robotics capabilities and limitations for optimal integration.
6. Link employees requiring a personal touch to formal learning or live subject matter experts.

7. Develop a shared standard way of operating to drive competence, confidence, and consistency across your organization.
8. Implement performance support tools to automate processes and improve employee efficiency.
9. Train employees how to include conversational and generative AI as functioning members of their teams and not just tools.
10. Ensure ethical design and implementation of AI systems with proper oversight and accountability.
11. Invest in algorithms that identify worker skills and competencies.
12. Modify worker profile tools to display work portfolios instead of job titles.
13. Reevaluate the recruiting process for the 21st-century workplace.
14. Gather a diverse mix of human and non-human team members across the organization.
15. Shift from traditional Human Resources to Transhuman Resources.
16. Align technology adoption with the organization's values.
17. Train talent management and institutions for modern workforce changes.
18. Use AI algorithms to reduce bias in the recruitment process and highlight job openings to underrepresented groups.
19. Monitor AI algorithms to prevent bias perpetuation and adjust them accordingly.
20. Develop ethical guidelines and policies for AI use in recruitment, emphasizing fairness, transparency, and accountability.
21. Shift HR practices to a skill- and performance-based decision process for an inclusive workforce of humans, augmented humans, and non-humans.

Chapter 9: The 3 Laws of Robotics

In 1942, Isaac Asimov proposed the "Three Laws of Robotics" in his science fiction novel "I, Robot". These laws were designed to prevent robots from harming humans and to act as a failsafe against catastrophic scenarios like a robot uprising. With the rise of AI and robotics in our daily lives, these laws have become more relevant than ever before.

Asimov's Three Laws of Robotics:

1. "A robot may not injure a human being or, through inaction, allow a human being to come to harm."
2. "A robot must obey the orders given it by human beings, except where such orders would conflict with the First Law."
3. "A robot must protect its own existence as long as such protection does not conflict with the First or Second Law."

Asimov's laws are simple and straightforward, but they raise complex questions about the intersection of AI and humanity. For instance, if we build a robot to help humans, how do we ensure that it won't cause harm in the process? If we give an AI assistant access to all our personal data, how can we be sure it won't use it against us?

As we continue to integrate AI and robotics into our daily lives, it is essential to consider the ethical implications of these technologies. We must establish a set of principles that govern the use of AI and robotics to protect human rights and ensure they are used for the greater good. To achieve this, we need to adopt a new set of principles that go beyond Asimov's Three Laws. These principles must take into account the complex and interconnected nature of our society and the impact our actions can have on the world around us.

Sustainable development

The concept of "sustainable development," introduced by the United Nations in 1987, provides a useful framework for thinking about how we can apply ethical principles to our use of AI and robotics. We must consider not just the short-term benefits of these technologies, but also their long-term impact on our society and the world at large.

We can ensure that everyone has the opportunity to participate in the benefits of these technologies by investing in the skills and knowledge of our workforce. This approach aligns with the concept of lifelong learning, which involves continuously developing new skills and knowledge to keep up with the pace of technological change and remain competitive in the workforce.

A framework for humanity

Ultimately, the Three Laws of Robotics provide a useful framework for thinking about the ethical implications of AI and robotics. As they become more widespread in our teams and workplaces, we need to apply the same laws to us as well, and consider the impact our actions have on our fellow humans and the world at large. We must ensure that our actions and decisions do not harm our fellow humans and that we are always acting in everyone's best interests. By adopting ethical principles that prioritize sustainability, reskilling, and upskilling, and applying them to both humans and AI, we can create a more harmonious and productive workplace, and a society that benefits all its members.

151

A fundamental shift in business

Applying the Three Laws of Robotics to humanity will require a fundamental shift in the way we think about our relationships with each other and with technology. It could lead to the creation of a work environment that prioritizes the safety and well-being of employees and customers above all else. It could also require companies to follow ethical and legal guidelines when making decisions that impact their stakeholders and to prioritize their long-term survival and success over short-term gains.

AI is becoming increasingly important for companies focused on long-term growth and value generation, but it also increases the impact of data risks and generates new risks, such as those from unintended consequences. Appropriate oversight by and guidance from the board or senior management can help to identify, assess, and manage these risks. It is important to remember that AI and robotics are not neutral technologies. They are created by humans and are shaped by our biases and values. This can lead to unintended consequences and reinforce existing social inequalities. To address this, we must prioritize diversity and inclusion in the development of AI and robotics and actively work to identify and mitigate bias in algorithms and data sets used to train these systems.

Furthermore, we need to ensure that AI and robotics are developed and used in a transparent and accountable manner. Company leaders should determine where and how AI is used throughout the organization. They need to evaluate whether the use of AI is appropriate, including assessing the ethical and other risks associated. Given the potential complexity of implementing AI, evaluating whether the leadership and the resources allocated to AI are adequate. Some organizations will need to consider engaging independent advisers to assist the company and/or the board throughout the business transformation and periodically revisit these elements. This means being upfront about the potential risks and limitations of these technologies and taking responsibility for any negative impacts they may have. It also means implementing mechanisms for oversight and regulation to ensure that these technologies are used in a way that benefits society.

In terms of business law, the application of the Three Laws of Robotics could lead to the development of new legal frameworks that prioritize the safety and well-being of all stakeholders, including the environment. It could also require companies to be more transparent and accountable for their actions and to provide greater access to information for their stakeholders. Additionally, companies should collaborate with their ecosystem of business partners, suppliers, customers, regulators, and other constituents to align on approaches to trustworthy AI. They should also assess whether their uses of AI are appropriate and achieving desired results, and if any unanticipated risks have been created. Finally, companies should communicate their principles and frameworks internally and externally to ensure they are embedded in AI initiatives.

Questions for organizations to consider asking include what is our AI strategy; what is our approach to AI governance; how are we driving trust in our company's use of AI; and how can AI impact our business now and in the future?

Action Items

1. Organizations should establish a set of ethical principles that govern the use of AI and robotics to protect human rights and ensure that these principles are used for the greater good.

2. Organizations should invest in the skills and knowledge of their workforce to ensure that everyone has the opportunity to participate in the benefits of these technologies.

3. Companies should prioritize diversity and inclusion in the development of AI and robotics and actively work to identify and mitigate bias in algorithms and data sets used to train these systems to ensure they are applied in a fair and equitable manner.

4. Companies should implement mechanisms for oversight and regulation to ensure that these technologies are used in a way that benefits society and informs everyone of the potential risks they may present.

5. Companies should collaborate with their ecosystem of business partners, suppliers, customers, regulators, and other constituents to align on approaches to trustworthy AI.

6. Company leaders should evaluate whether the leadership and resources allocated to AI are adequate and consider engaging independent advisers to assist the company and/or the board.

7. Companies should communicate their principles and frameworks internally and externally to ensure they are embedded in AI initiatives.

8. Companies should ask questions like "what is our AI strategy?"; "what is our approach to AI governance?"; "how are we driving trust in our company's use of AI?"; and "how can AI impact our business now and in the future?"

Chapter 10: Mental Health in the Age of AI

The integration of artificial intelligence in our daily lives has brought about many benefits, including increased efficiency, accuracy, and convenience. From the virtual assistants on our smartphones to the recommendation systems on our streaming services, AI technology is integrated in many ways. AI and robotics have enabled significant advancements in various industries, from manufacturing to healthcare. However, as AI technology becomes more advanced, machines may begin to develop emotions and consciousness, which can have ethical implications including concerns about the potential impact on mental health, both for humans and for our machine counterparts as we integrate them further into our society.

Positives

On the positive side, AI technology has helped doctors and researchers to identify diseases, develop new treatments, and even predict outbreaks of diseases. In transportation, AI technology has been used to develop self-driving cars that can reduce the number of accidents caused by human error. In finance, AI technology has helped to detect fraud and prevent financial crimes.

Negatives

The negative side, however, raises concerns regarding mental health as a result of the influx of AI, robotics, and human augmentation due to the loss of purpose that can come with the increased automation of certain jobs and tasks. As machines become more advanced and capable of taking on a wider range of roles, there is a risk that some people will feel left behind or redundant. This can lead to feelings of depression, anxiety, and a sense of hopelessness.

Root causes

The use of AI, generative AI, and cobots in personal and business settings are now under study for the potential to bring about various mental health issues. Many of these have similarities to other online services like social media, streaming content, and even hybrid or work from home situations and must be evaluated across a person's full psychological profile to determine the root cause(s). Some of these potential issues include:

Anxiety

The rapid advancements in AI and cobot technology may lead to increased feelings of anxiety in individuals, as they may worry about job security, privacy concerns, and the ethical implications of using AI.

Depression

The potential loss of jobs due to automation and AI could lead to feelings of hopelessness, loss of purpose, and depression in affected individuals.

Social isolation

As AI and cobots take on more tasks in both personal and professional settings, people may have fewer opportunities to engage in social interactions, leading to loneliness and social isolation.

Stress

The pressure to adapt to new technologies, learn new skills, or compete with AI and cobots can cause increased stress levels in individuals.

Technostress

The constant exposure to and reliance on technology may lead to psychological distress or "technostress," negatively impacting some people.

Addiction

People may develop an unhealthy dependency on AI-driven devices and services for personal or professional purposes, leading to addiction-like behaviors.

Decreased self-esteem

Comparing oneself to the perceived perfection and efficiency of AI systems and cobots may result in feelings of inadequacy and decreased self-esteem.

Imposter syndrome

Individuals working alongside AI and cobots may feel like they are not as competent or knowledgeable as the technology, leading to imposter syndrome.

Cognitive overload

The influx of information and data generated by AI and cobot technologies can lead to cognitive overload, making it difficult for individuals to process information and make decisions.

Moral distress

The ethical concerns surrounding AI and cobot usage may cause moral distress for some individuals, as they struggle to reconcile their personal values with the implications of the technology.

It is important to be aware of these potential mental health issues and provide support, education, and resources to help individuals cope with the challenges presented by AI and cobot integration in personal and professional settings.

A loss of purpose

Many people derive a sense of self-worth from their work and the contributions they make to society. When their jobs are automated or outsourced, they may feel that they have lost a significant part of their identity, leading to feelings of worthlessness and isolation. As a result, a loss of purpose may lead to stress and anxiety in individuals, which can have a negative impact on their mental health.

Pandemic exposed limits

The COVID-19 pandemic has caused unprecedented disruptions across the world, affecting all aspects of human life. One of the most significant impacts has been on technology and its role in enabling remote work, virtual connections, and AI-powered solutions. While these advancements have been instrumental in ensuring business continuity and communication during the pandemic, they have also highlighted some significant issues related to technology dependency and its adverse effects on human lives.

One of the most critical issues that have been exacerbated by the pandemic is technology addiction. With the widespread adoption of virtual connections and remote devices, people have become increasingly reliant on technology to stay connected, work, and entertain themselves. As a result, many people have become addicted to social media, video games, and other online platforms, leading to mental health issues, such as anxiety and depression.

Another big problem is the impact of remote work and virtual connections on the workforce. While remote work has been beneficial in many ways, it has also exposed the digital divide and unequal access to technology. Workers who do not have access to reliable internet connections, suitable workspaces, and essential equipment may find it challenging to work remotely. This issue has particularly affected low-income workers and those living in rural areas.

To make matters even more complicated, the pandemic has also exposed the limitations of AI-powered solutions. While AI has been used extensively in various fields to automate processes and improve efficiency, it has also demonstrated its lack of human intelligence and flexibility. For instance, in the healthcare industry, AI-powered systems may struggle to diagnose complex medical conditions accurately, leading to potentially fatal consequences.

Moreover, the pandemic has also highlighted the security risks associated with technology dependency. With the increase in virtual connections and remote devices, there has been a surge in cyberattacks, data breaches, and online scams. Cybercriminals have taken advantage of the pandemic to exploit vulnerabilities in remote networks and steal sensitive data.

In addition, the increasing reliance on technology can have an impact on our attention span and ability to focus. The constant stream of notifications, emails, and messages can make it difficult to concentrate and can lead to feelings of being overwhelmed and ever increasing anxiety.

Physicians heal thyself

Of course, with the recent flurry of activity, the application of AI to address the rising mental issues seems counter intuitive. However, in a recent pilot study conducted at the University of Illinois, researchers had patient volunteers use Lumen, an AI voice assistant, to deliver a form of psychotherapy, which led to improved depression and anxiety symptoms in patients. The UIC study reported changes in the brain activity of patients, particularly increased activity in the dorsolateral prefrontal cortex, an area associated with cognitive control. The researchers emphasize that while Lumen and similar technology can't replace human therapists, they can help bridge the gap between supply and demand in mental health care.

Human connection and support

To address these concerns and mitigate the potential impact on mental health, it is important to prioritize human connection and support. While technology can provide many benefits, it cannot replace the emotional support and validation that comes from genuine human interaction. We need to prioritize social relationships and find ways to foster connections even in a world that is increasingly digital and automated. This can include setting aside time for social activities, such as video chats, online games, and virtual social events. It can mean investing in relationships with family, friends, and colleagues, and making an effort to stay connected, even when we are busy or stressed.

One way to combat the loss of purpose and identity is by encouraging individuals to explore new interests and hobbies outside of work. This can help them find a sense of purpose and fulfillment in their personal lives, which can carry over into their professional lives.

Furthermore, employers can play a crucial role in supporting their employees' mental health by offering mental health resources and support systems including access to counseling or therapy services, offering flexible work arrangements, or implementing wellness programs.

Effective communication

There are also concerns about the impact of AI and machine learning on our ability to communicate effectively. As we rely more on digital communication and automated systems, we may lose some of the social skills that are crucial for building and maintaining relationships. This could lead to increased feelings of social isolation and difficulty in forming meaningful connections with others.

What's more, the spread of fake news and the manipulation of digital twins (virtual replicas of people or objects) can contribute to a sense of distrust and segregation within society. When we can no longer trust the information, we receive or the authenticity of those around us, it can lead to feelings of anxiety and a breakdown in social cohesion.

Healthy digital habits

So, what can we do to address these concerns and ensure that the integration of AI and technology is beneficial for both our mental health and our overall well-being?

We can work to promote healthy digital habits and encourage people to use technology in a way that is beneficial for their mental health. Diagnosis of mental issues may result in setting boundaries around social media use or finding ways to incorporate more in-person interactions into our daily routines.

Investing in mental health

We must continue to invest in mental health resources and support systems. As the impact of AI on mental health becomes better understood, we can work to develop new tools and strategies for addressing these challenges. Organizations may need to expand access to mental health services, provide mental health education and resources, and create safe spaces for people to share their experiences and feelings. And, while technology dependency is a contributing issue, it can also be a benefit when used for the development of AI-powered mental health apps or chatbots, or the integration of mental health support into existing digital tools and platforms.

Brain wearables

The desire to monitor one's own health is important to wellbeing and preventative care. New wearable medical devices from Fitbit and Apple seem to be emerging daily. Now, an influx of brain-tracking devices is expected to enter the market soon, with tech giants like Meta, Snap, Microsoft, and Apple investing heavily in this technology. These wearables could revolutionize healthcare by enabling early diagnosis and personalized treatment of various conditions, as well as improving meditation, focus, and communication. However, they also pose significant risks to mental privacy, freedom of thought, and self-determination, as they generate vast amounts of neural data. Employers are increasingly using this data to monitor worker fatigue, wellness, and cognitive abilities, potentially eroding trust, well-being, and the dignity of work. Safeguards must be implemented to protect individuals' mental privacy as brain wearables become more widespread.

Governments are showing interest in accessing brain data for various purposes, including understanding neurological conditions and developing brain biometric programs. However, this could lead to government interference with freedom of thought and a future of brain surveillance. The advancement of brain wearables and AI raises questions about human control, as the line between human decision-making and machine intervention blurs. Overdependence on technology could weaken independent thought and reflective decision-making. Moreover, there are risks of malicious use and hacking of brain wearables, which could lead to privacy breaches and manipulation. Companies in China have already accumulated vast amounts of brain data, highlighting the need for security measures and data safeguards to protect mental privacy and ensure the beneficial use of neurotechnology.

Action Items

1. Assess the current impact of AI and automation on the workforce and identify jobs at high risk of automation.
2. Develop a comprehensive mental health support program addressing anxiety, depression, social isolation, stress, technostress, addiction, decreased self-esteem, imposter syndrome, cognitive overload, and moral distress.
3. Provide access to mental health resources for employees affected by AI and cobot integration.
4. Organize workshops and training sessions to help employees adapt to new technologies and develop relevant skills.
5. Create opportunities for social interaction and team-building activities to counteract social isolation effects.
6. Encourage a healthy work-life balance and establish boundaries between personal and professional technology use.
7. Develop strategies to ensure equal access to technology, resources, and training for all employees.
8. Implement robust cybersecurity measures to protect employee data and maintain the integrity of remote networks and AI-powered systems.
9. Promote open communication and provide a platform for employees to discuss ethical implications of AI and cobot integration.
10. Collaborate with industry experts, academic institutions, and government agencies to stay updated on AI advancements, ethical concerns, and best practices.
11. Evaluate and modify company policies to support employees during transitions and job displacement due to AI and automation.

12. Foster a culture of continuous learning and development, encouraging employees to upskill and reskill.
13. Develop and implement a digital well-being program to promote healthy digital habits, work-life balance, time management, and mindfulness.
14. Offer training and workshops on managing technology dependency and identifying early signs of mental health issues.
15. Encourage virtual and in-person social interactions and team-building activities to foster connections among employees.
16. Establish a comprehensive mental health support system, including access to counseling services, support groups, and educational materials.
17. Collaborate with employees to identify areas of concern and potential improvements in remote work conditions and technology use.
18. Regularly assess the impact of AI, virtual connections, and remote devices on the workforce and adapt policies and resources accordingly.
19. Enhance cybersecurity measures and educate employees on best practices to ensure data protection and network security.
20. Address the digital divide by providing equal access to technology, resources, and training for all employees, promoting inclusivity and equal opportunities.

Chapter 11: The Gig Economy

The world is currently witnessing a transformational shift in the employment landscape due to the widespread adoption of automation and artificial intelligence (AI) in the workplace. While these technologies have brought about many benefits such as increased efficiency, accuracy, and productivity, they have also created a high level of uncertainty among employees who fear being displaced by machines.

One of the main reasons for this uncertainty is the sheer speed at which automation and AI are advancing. Machines are becoming increasingly sophisticated, able to perform tasks that were previously thought to be the exclusive domain of humans. From self-driving cars to chatbots, machines are taking over more and more jobs every day, and the pace of change shows no signs of slowing down.

In the face of this rapid change, many workers are understandably worried about their job security. They fear that their jobs will be automated, rendering them obsolete and leaving them without a source of income. This fear is particularly acute in industries where machines are already beginning to replace human workers, such as manufacturing and transportation.

Furthermore, the rise of the gig economy has further complicated the employment landscape. Freelance and contract work are becoming increasingly popular, but they come with their own set of challenges. Workers in the gig economy have less job security, fewer benefits, and less stability than traditional employees. The rise of the gig economy has also made it more difficult for workers to form unions or other forms of collective bargaining, which can help protect workers' rights.

The future is bright

Despite these challenges, there are reasons to be optimistic about the future of work. While it is true that automation and AI are replacing some jobs, they are also creating new ones. For example, the rise of automation has created a demand for workers who can design, program, and maintain machines. Similarly, the development of AI has led to the creation of new jobs in areas such as data science and machine learning.

Now, add to this the support AI provides for the hobbyist and do-it-yourselfer now wanting to be entrepreneur. In a recent New York Times article, they outline just a few of the personal uses for AI and robotics. Some are using it to enhance their lives and save time at work, code without knowing how to code, and make daily life easier. Others are using AI to plan gardens and workouts, design parts for spaceships and organize messy computer desktops. The applications of AI appear to be endless like being used to create games, code them, and even name them. It can also provide justification for its decisions. AI is being used to search for a malaria vaccine and Parkinson's research. AI can predict the shape of proteins and generate examples of how they should look. It is making it easier and faster to create new proteins and games, as well as providing better coaching for sports like curling. I personally use it to draft reports and have recently got it creating dad jokes (even worse than my own).

Fortunately, there is a growing recognition among policymakers and business leaders that the adoption of automation and AI must be done in a way that benefits workers, rather than simply maximizing profits. This means investing in education and training programs that will help workers acquire the skills they need to succeed in the jobs of the future. It also means providing workers with social safety nets such as long-term unemployment insurance and healthcare benefits, which can help cushion the impact of job displacement.

A shadow of uncertainty

The current employment landscape is characterized by unprecedented levels of uncertainty. According to a recent survey, 60% of employees believe that few people will have stable, long-term employment in the future. The advent of automation and artificial intelligence (AI) has only added to the anxiety, with 37% of employees expressing concern about the risk of job displacement. In this climate of uncertainty, it's not surprising that 70% of employees are willing to consider brain and body-enhancing treatments or augmentation to improve their job prospects in the future.

One of the most significant concerns surrounding the rise of automation and AI is the fear that these technologies will replace human workers. However, this concern may be overblown. While it is true that automation and AI have the potential to replace some jobs, it's important to remember that these technologies are not a panacea. For example, if a company applies machine learning to train one AI "employee," it can produce as many copies as needed. However, without humans to purchase the products and services provided by these automated systems, the value of these systems is greatly diminished.

In late 2020, large language models (LLMs) became a catalyst for rapid change as they reached a maturity level to have the potential to significantly affect a diverse range of occupations within the US economy. They have enabled artificial intelligence (AI) and more specifically natural language processing

170

(NLP) to be classified as a general-purpose technology. These LLMs are improving in capabilities over time and have pervasive impacts across the economy. A 2023 study conducted by OpenAI and the University of Pennsylvania, examined the potential of General-Purpose Transformers (GPTs) to disrupt US labor markets and found that 19% of jobs have at least 50% of their tasks exposed to GPTs, with higher-wage occupations generally presenting more tasks with high exposure. Occupations with the highest exposure include interpreters and translators, survey researchers, poets, lyricists and creative writers, public relations specialists, writers and authors, mathematicians, programmers, court reporters and simultaneous captioners, proofreaders and copy markers, and correspondence clerks. Tasks that require a high degree of human interaction, precise measurements, reviewing visuals in detail, any use of a hand or walking, or making decisions that might impact human livelihood have little to no concern for automation.

Moreover, the idea that robots will replace human workers overlooks the fact that automation and AI can create new opportunities and industries. In fact, a recent study by the McKinsey Global Institute found that AI has the potential to create new jobs that are currently unimaginable. These new jobs will require a different set of skills and competencies than those that are currently in demand, which underscores the importance of lifelong learning and reskilling.

To ensure that workers are equipped to thrive in the future of work, it's important to prioritize education and training. Employers must provide employees with opportunities to learn new skills and technologies, as well as support for ongoing development. This can take many forms, from tuition reimbursement programs to on-the-job training and mentorship.

The gig economy and side hustles

The gig economy is rapidly expanding, with more and more people choosing to work as freelancers, independent contractors, or in short-term contracts rather than in traditional employment. According to a recent study by Intuit, by 2020, 43% of the U.S. workforce will be made up of gig workers.

The term 'gig economy' is used to describe a flexible work environment where individuals are paid for their time and effort instead of working full-time, permanent jobs. The gig economy has revolutionized the traditional approach to employment, giving individuals more control over their work schedule and income. It has also enabled people to pursue their interests and passions by allowing them to conduct side hustles. Side hustles have become increasingly popular in recent years, with people taking up added jobs to supplement their primary income.

The gig economy has been on the rise since the early 2000s, and the trend has only accelerated in recent years. According to a report by McKinsey, in the US, the gig economy has grown by nearly 30% over the past decade, and the number of people working in the gig economy is expected to exceed 60 million by 2024. The rise of the gig economy can be attributed to several factors, including the growth of the internet, the need for flexibility, economic uncertainty, and the desire for increased control over work schedules. Layoffs in this decade have become common, leaving many people without permanent jobs. In such a scenario, the gig economy has provided an opportunity for individuals to earn money through side-hustles and temporary jobs. It has also allowed businesses to access a flexible workforce to meet their immediate needs without the long-term commitment of hiring full-time employees.

Side-hustles can be anything from freelancing, consulting, or even starting a small business. They provide individuals with the opportunity to pursue their passions and interests outside of their primary job while also earning extra income. In some cases, they have even turned into full-time careers, enabling individuals to achieve financial independence.

The flip side of it all is that the rise of the gig economy is having a significant impact on traditional employment. It has led to a shift in power from employers to employees, with individuals having more control over their work schedule and income. This shift has also forced companies to adapt to the changing needs of the workforce, with many organizations offering flexible work arrangements to attract and retain talent. It is also due to a decline in job security, with many workers relying on multiple sources of income to make ends meet. For many workers this is not a new situation. Blue collar service, or even those in the education field, have faced having one, two, or even three jobs to stay ahead. What is new is that it is now affecting everyone, including white collar jobs like business management and information technology.

Advances in technology have made it easier than ever for individuals to work from anywhere in the world, opening new opportunities for independent workers and small virtual teams. This has also enabled businesses to access a global pool of talent and reduce their labor costs, thus increasing competition for jobs with individuals from all over the world competing for the same opportunities. As the gig economy continues to grow, it is becoming increasingly important for workers to demonstrate their skills and qualifications to potential employers.

What's wrong with vocational schools

As the world progresses and industries evolve, so do the skills and talents required to keep up with the pace. The shortage of skilled workers is not a new phenomenon, and history has shown that it can lead to rapid advancement and opportunity for those willing to step up to the challenge. Achieving consistency and effectiveness in a global skills market means ensuring that all students have equal access and quality of education. This requires a concerted effort to develop and implement vocational education programs that are accessible to all students, regardless of their background or socioeconomic status. It also requires ongoing collaboration between vocational schools, community colleges, universities, and businesses to ensure that students are learning the most up-to-date skills. And it requires a willingness to experiment with new approaches to education and to be flexible in response to changing market demands.

After World War II, the shortage of talent was palpable. Much like Millennials today, younger workers were thrust into management positions to help bring the economy back around. It was a time of uncertainty, but also one of immense opportunity for those willing to take on the challenge. This is a testament to the resilience and adaptability of the human spirit in times of crisis.

In the late 1960s, the launch of new technology, computers, brought about an incredible shortage of programmers. With so few college graduates in this new field, IBM, GTE, and other technology giants had to find candidates that showed aptitude and hire them without degrees. They then trained these candidates on the job, leading to a new wave of talent in the computer programming industry.

Today, we see a similar cycle happening in the areas of Machine Learning, AI, robotics, 3D printing, energy generation, and sustainable farming. As technology advances and industries shift, the need for skilled workers in these areas continues to grow. However, the pipeline for traditional talent may not be able to keep up with the pace of change.

At the same time, educational institutions must adapt to the changing needs of the labor market. This means that community colleges, vocational schools, and universities must work more closely with employers to develop curricula that reflect the demands of the twenty-first-century workplace. This partnership can help ensure that students are equipped with the skills and competencies needed to succeed in the workforce and that employers have access to a pipeline of qualified talent.

To fill the talent pipeline, industries are reaching out earlier to prepare talent in middle school and high school with a resurgence of vocational education classes in advanced skills like manufacturing and programming. Vocational schools and community colleges are partnering directly with consortia of organizations to ensure consistency of skills. However, there are still challenges that need to be addressed to prepare students and employees for jobs in the 21st century.

Skills over degrees

One of the main issues with traditional education is the lack of consistency in skills development. With industries changing rapidly and new technologies emerging all the time, it is important that students are trained in the most up-to-date skills. This requires collaboration between vocational schools, community colleges, universities, and businesses to ensure that students are learning the hands-on skills that will be in demand in the job market.

Employers are seeking out individuals who have shown aptitude and interest in these emerging fields, even if they do not have traditional degrees or experience. This creates a unique opportunity for individuals to break into these industries and carve out a new career path. However, it also puts pressure on employers to be more innovative in their hiring and training practices. They must be willing to take a chance on individuals with potential and invest in their development. This is a shift away from traditional recruiting practices and requires a willingness to adapt to new methods. It is a chance for individuals to seize new opportunities and for organizations to rethink their approach to talent acquisition and development.

Diversity includes skills and perspectives

One potential approach to promoting inclusivity in the workplace is to create diverse teams with a range of skills and perspectives. These teams should be empowered to work independently and make decisions based on the best interests of the business.

2020 will be known as the year of diversity and inclusion – no longer bound by race, gender, age, language, disability, area of specialization, etc. Now, with the growing set of human enhancement technologies may allow us to physically or, through the Metaverse, virtually be whatever we want with whatever capabilities we desire. Talent Management must proactively develop new policies, practices, and tools to enable organizations to manage and develop transhuman and non-human resources effectively or run the risk of being ill prepared as the transformation unfolds. Looking back on diversity, equity, and inclusion (DEI), how many legal and staffing issues could have been avoided if we had only had the foresight to address the unintended consequences related to large scale implementation in businesses around the world?

Unlike cobots and AI, humans are social creatures. We tend to flock to those like us. We have seen a push by some to homogenize all social groups and eliminate segregation even when it is for good - imagine no more gyms exclusively for a specific gender or all sports becoming unisex. However, in a world without boundaries, people will invent their own, especially when dealing with differences that lead to jealousy or removal of positions or status. Rather than haphazardly creating these new social constructs, we should use inclusiveness as a deliberate action to create areas of mutual interest. We need to construct specific business-oriented boundaries to provide environments for diverse teams to foster successful innovation.

The power of a generative AI team

Generative AI is the 2023 equivalent of desktop publishing. Now, anyone with creativity and drive can create amazing content without requiring an entire team of skilled specialists. And, even if they do need those specialists to polish the product, the early work can be cost effectively generated and then iterated until it is ready for the final step. All this happening at little to no cost, thus increasing the margins for the gig employee. This enabler is leveling the playing field in yet another way thanks to AI.

If you add to this 3D printing or cobot manufacturing, marketing, shipping, and automated business processes, a one-person shop is now truly possible (and scalable). This is the era for entrepreneurs and small businesses to flourish. Businesses large and small need to recognize the power an AI team can have in the marketplace.

Not just a numbers game

Finally, it's important to recognize that the future of work is not just a numbers game. While automation and AI will undoubtedly have a significant impact on the labor market, they are not the only factors driving change. Other factors, such as shifting demographics and globalization, are also influencing the way we work. Therefore, it's essential to approach the future of work holistically, recognizing the interconnectedness of these various trends and taking a proactive approach to managing change.

Until 2014, most major machine learning models were developed by academics. Since then, industry has taken the lead. In 2022, there were 32 significant machine learning models created by industry compared to only three from academia. Constructing the most advanced AI systems necessitates a great deal of data, computing power, and money - resources that industry has more of than non-profits and academics.

It is no longer possible to hide from the future under the constraints of the past. Companies and institutions large and small can adapt and adopt these changes. Being risk averse in implementing these rapidly evolving technologies may put you and your organization at risk - especially of falling behind.

Action Items

1. Invest in upskilling and reskilling programs to help employees adapt to the evolving employment landscape.
2. Implement mentorship programs and career guidance services to support employees in navigating career transitions.
3. Develop and promote flexible work arrangements to attract and retain talent in the face of the gig economy.
4. Establish a support system for gig workers, including access to benefits, training, and resources.
5. Foster a culture of lifelong learning, continuous development, and collaboration within the organization.
6. Work with industry experts, academic institutions, and government agencies to stay updated on emerging trends in the employment landscape.
7. Advocate for responsible adoption of AI and automation, emphasizing human-centered design and ethical considerations.
8. Promote employee well-being and mental health, addressing concerns related to job security and the impact of automation.
9. Create opportunities for employees to develop side hustles within the organization, providing resources and support for entrepreneurial endeavors.
10. Strengthen communication and transparency around AI and automation strategies, ensuring employee involvement in decision-making processes.

11. Develop partnerships with organizations and educational institutions to create a talent pipeline for emerging roles in AI, automation, and high-growth areas.

12. Create educational programs to raise awareness among gig workers about the benefits of using technology for showcasing their skills.

13. Foster partnerships between vocational schools, community colleges, universities, and businesses to develop curricula reflecting the demands of the 21st-century workplace.

14. Implement diversity and inclusion policies that consider the unique skill sets and backgrounds of gig workers in the global talent pool.

15. Stay informed about the latest trends in automation, AI, and other factors influencing the future of work, and proactively adjust HR strategies accordingly.

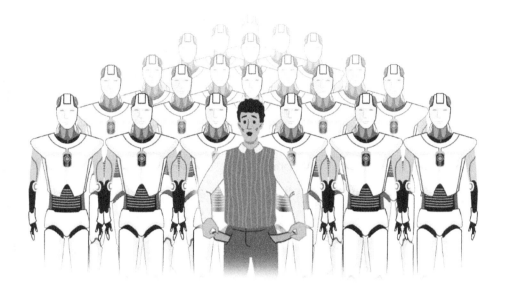

Chapter 12: A Zero-Sum Game

The emergence of technological advancements such as AI, robotics, and human enhancements has opened a world of possibilities for humankind. However, amidst all these exciting developments, it is crucial to remember that we still need a human touch to ensure that our society thrives. As we embrace automation and AI, we should strive to find ways to maximize resource yields and optimize resource utilization to benefit everyone.

It is essential to acknowledge that there is a cost associated with creating and developing these solutions. We often view successful companies or individuals as overnight sensations without considering the years of hard work that went into their achievements. We must compensate these creators adequately and recognize the value they bring to our society.

As we shift into this new world, we need to ensure that everyone participates equally. One potential solution to this is to provide each person with the same resources, such as a 3D-printed modular home, groceries from automated farms, and robots to handle cleaning services. However, once we achieve this level of comfort, will there be any motivation to drive the next generation of innovation? Can humanity exist without hierarchy and struggle, which often serve as catalysts for change and evolution?

While a Utopian society may sound ideal, it is not without its flaws. We must strike a balance between our dependence on automation and our need for exertion. The phrase "no pain, no gain" is a common euphemism that can lead to tragedy if taken to extremes. History, however, demonstrates natural struggle can lead to some of humanity's biggest accomplishments.

Control and balance

As we covered earlier in this book, there are concerns around the impact of automation and AI on employment. As more tasks are automated, some jobs may become redundant, leading to job losses in certain industries. Machines can help us achieve wonders we have only imagined as long as we work with them and not for them. Otherwise, we may one day find ourselves cleaning their toilets. As Yuval Noah Harari, a historian at the Hebrew University of Jerusalem, pointed out, "What should we do with all the potentially unemployable class of people, once we have AI that can do almost everything better than humans?" This question highlights a significant concern regarding the impact of automation on the job market and the economy. It is up to us to ensure that we maintain control and balance in this new age.

One thing this view overlooks is the fact that machines are only capable of performing tasks that they have been programmed to do. Even with the advent of generative AI, someone still needs to provide the prompts to start the generation. Based on the resulting outputs and a variety of other objective and subjective feedback, modifications to these prompts may be required. Humans have the ability to learn and adapt to new situations, solve problems creatively, and form interpersonal connections. Thus, it is crucial to view machines not as a replacement for humans, but rather as partners. Machines can perform repetitive and mundane tasks, freeing up humans to focus on more creative and strategic work that requires human skills and expertise. This partnership between humans and machines has the potential to unlock new levels of innovation and productivity that were previously unattainable.

Another reason why machines should be viewed as partners is that they can help to improve safety and reduce the risk of accidents. Certain tasks, such as working with hazardous chemicals or heavy machinery, can be dangerous for humans. By delegating these tasks to machines, humans can reduce their exposure to potential harm, while still reaping the benefits of the work being done.

Here are some real-world examples of balance and control related to the emergence of AI and robotics in the workforce:

Amazon's robotic fulfillment centers

Amazon has implemented a system of robotic fulfillment centers that work alongside human workers to improve efficiency and productivity. The robots are designed to handle repetitive and physically demanding tasks, while human workers oversee the process and handle more complex tasks.

JPMorgan Chase's contract intelligence system

JPMorgan Chase has developed an AI-powered system that can review legal documents and extract important information, such as key terms and clauses. The system is designed to save time and reduce errors, while still allowing human lawyers to review and approve the final documents.

Ford's collaborative robots

Ford has implemented a system of collaborative robots, or "cobots," that work alongside human workers to improve efficiency and safety in their manufacturing plants. The cobots are designed to handle repetitive and physically demanding tasks, while human workers oversee the process and handle more complex tasks.

IBM's AI ethics board

IBM has established an AI Ethics Board to oversee the development and deployment of their AI systems. The board is made up of experts in AI, ethics, and policy, and is responsible for ensuring that IBM's AI systems are developed and used in a responsible and ethical manner.

These examples demonstrate how businesses are implementing balance and control measures to ensure that AI and robotics are used in a responsible and ethical manner. They show how AI and robotics can work alongside human workers to improve efficiency and productivity, while still maintaining human oversight and control.

The biggest problem with the machine vs. man conundrum is more fundamental. It is an economic problem known as a zero-sum game.

A zero-sum game

A zero-sum game is a situation in which one person's gain is another person's loss, and the total sum of gains and losses equals zero. In the context of automation and the job market, the zero-sum game is often used to argue that the replacement of human workers by robots will result in the displacement of a significant portion of the workforce, leading to widespread unemployment and economic instability. However, this argument fails to account for the interconnectedness and interdependence of humanity.

185

We are becoming increasingly interdependent, with all parts making up the whole. The rise of transhumanism and associated technological advancements has blurred the lines between humans and machines, creating a symbiotic relationship between the two. Automation and AI have the potential to free us from mundane and repetitive tasks, allowing us to focus on more complex and creative work. This partnership, in turn, can lead to increased productivity, innovation, and economic growth. However, it is essential to remember that these advancements are not meant to replace humans but to work in conjunction with us.

The concept of a zero-sum game assumes that the economy is a closed system with limited resources. However, this is not the case. The economy is an open system, constantly evolving and adapting to new technologies and changes in the market. While it is true that certain jobs may become obsolete, new opportunities will arise in fields such as robotics engineering, maintenance, data science, and programming. Additionally, the freed-up labor force can be redirected towards new and more innovative industries, creating new economic opportunities and driving growth. As we have seen throughout history, technological advancements have always led to the creation of new jobs and industries, not the displacement of workers.

Consider this, if all human workers were to be replaced by robots, who would be left to buy the products and services created by these machines? This is where the interdependence of humanity comes into play. The economy relies on consumer demand, and without humans consuming the products and services created by robots, the entire system will collapse. Therefore, it is in the best interest of businesses and policymakers to ensure that automation and AI work in tandem with human labor, creating a balanced system that benefits everyone.

Action Items

1. Assess the impact of AI and automation on existing job roles and identify areas where human skills are irreplaceable.
2. Develop and implement retraining programs for employees whose roles may be affected by automation, focusing on developing skills needed in emerging industries.
3. Encourage collaboration between humans and machines to maximize efficiency and innovation in the workplace.
4. Prioritize employee well-being and mental health, recognizing the potential stressors associated with rapid technological advancements.
5. Foster a culture of continuous learning and adaptation to prepare employees for the evolving workplace landscape.
6. Establish ethical guidelines for the use of AI and automation to ensure the responsible integration of technology in the workplace.
7. Promote diversity and inclusion to ensure that everyone has equal access to opportunities created by technological advancements.
8. Advocate for the development of policies and regulations that protect workers from potential negative consequences of automation and AI.
9. Monitor the implementation of AI and automation in the workplace to ensure that it complements human skills rather than replacing them.
10. Engage in open dialogues with employees, management, and stakeholders to address concerns and share insights about the evolving role of humans in the age of AI and automation.

Chapter 13: It's All About Us

As far as we know, humans are the only species on the planet to truly fear the future and not just anticipate natural disasters in a fight or flight mode. We are also the only species we know of that is optimistic - we recognize the opportunities that disruptions like these provide. I for one am excited by the changes we are already experiencing and the ones that are coming sooner than many are willing to accept.

As we have seen throughout the pages and stories in this book, the metamorphosis of collaboration across various domains is here and now and it's all about us. The dynamic interplay between humans, augmented humans, and non-humans, and the ways in which these partnerships are reshaping business, society, are redefining the very essence of what it means to be human. By understanding the nuances and potential of these relationships, you can now develop insights into how to best adapt and thrive today and in the years to come.

Humans possess a unique capacity to both fear and be optimistic about the future, recognizing the opportunities that disruptive change offers. This ability sets us apart from other species on the planet, allowing us to anticipate natural disasters and adapt accordingly. The increasing collaboration between humans, augmented humans, and non-humans is transforming various domains, redefining the essence of what it means to be human. By understanding the nuances and potential of these relationships, we can adapt to the evolving landscape and thrive in the coming years.

The integration of artificial intelligence, human augmentation, and robotics in our workforce holds the potential to revolutionize industries and improve the overall quality of life for numerous individuals. AI is already delivering real social and economic benefits for people, from helping doctors identify diseases faster to aiding farmers in using their land more efficiently and sustainably. Adopting AI in more sectors could improve productivity and unlock growth, which is why governments should commit to unleashing AI's potential across the economy.

Companies that successfully integrate humans and machines will gain a strategic advantage in the future market, so it is vital to provide training and education to ensure employees have the skills they need to thrive in this new environment. It is essential for businesses to continuously evaluate the potential impact of using or not using evolving technology solutions to stay competitive. Recent data indicates that companies adopting AI and cobots have experienced significant productivity gains, cost reductions, and revenue increases across various business and manufacturing functions.

Human resource practices must also evolve to keep up with the changing needs of the workforce. HR leaders must shift their organizations to a skill- and performance-based decision process, ensuring inclusivity in the workplace as the world becomes more diverse. Traditional human resources should evolve to transhuman resources to accommodate an inclusive workforce of humans, augmented humans, and non-humans.

Governments, corporations, researchers, and civil society must collaborate to shape our future in a manner that reflects our shared values and aspirations. Policymakers, technologists, and businesses must develop a comprehensive framework that balances innovation with ethical considerations. By doing so, we can create a future that is not only technologically advanced but also socially just and equitable.

Human augmentation is expanding at an incredible pace, and we must proceed with caution, ensuring that we use these technologies ethically and responsibly. Equitable distribution is crucial to avoid a new age of classism based on augmented or non-augmented individuals. We should not shy away from improving our capabilities, but we must account for them in both personal and business decisions. As we move forward, we must continue to explore the potential benefits and challenges of human augmentation, working towards a future that prioritizes the well-being of all individuals.

To ensure that the rise of advanced technologies benefits everyone, education and training programs should be provided so that all individuals can learn about and benefit from the latest advancements in technology. Reskilling and upskilling are necessary for individuals to keep up with the rapidly changing job market. Companies can support this by providing training in multiple formats, such as extended reality and generative AI, which offer more efficient and accessible training options, and by supporting side-hustles.

The future of work is rapidly evolving, and organizations must adapt to stay competitive. Businesses need to gather a diverse mix of human, augmented human, and non-human employees across all parts of their organizations, taking active steps to align with forward-thinking strategies and making inclusion a key part of their teams. Successful companies will tackle complex problems with elegant solutions generated by the combination of multiple minds, including those made of silicon and code. Virtual, work-from-home, and hybrid environments make this mix even more important and challenging, as we use telepresence for collaboration and to run manufacturing operations remotely in factories or the field with the aid of cobots.

As our roles in this new world shift, we need to balance our dependence on automation with our need for exertion. A truly successful society requires everyone to participate equally. We must ask ourselves whether we should strive for a world where everyone starts with the same resources and opportunities, much like in the game of Monopoly, and allow individuals to achieve success based on their choices and actions. This could go as far as providing essential resources, such as 3D printed modular homes, groceries from automated local farms, solar and wind power, robotic cleaning services, and shared electric vehicles, among other amenities.

Once we are all in our comfort zone, will there still be a driving force for the next generation of innovation? Can humanity exist without hierarchy and struggle to serve as catalysts for change and evolution? The concept of Utopia might seem ideal on paper, but the reality might be far from perfect. As a species, we need to strike a balance between relying on automation and embracing natural struggle. Natural struggle can also lead to our most significant accomplishments. Machines can help us achieve wonders we have only imagined if we work with them, not for them. Otherwise, we might find ourselves serving them well into the future.

Imagine, if you will, a world where the unique strengths of humans, augmented humans, and non-humans are seamlessly woven together, creating a rich tapestry of shared innovation, empathy, and potential. Imagine a future where our

193

collective abilities are harnessed to not only revolutionize industries but also address the pressing challenges of our time—from climate change to inequality. Imagine by fostering a culture of inclusivity, prioritizing education and training, and maintaining a focus on mental health and well-being, we can navigate the challenges and opportunities presented by this new era. I hope you will take what you have learned from this book and use the key takeaways to help guide you, sparking your curiosity, igniting debate in your communities and workplaces, and inspiring in you a sense of wonder. As the previous chapters have demonstrated, the human factor remains essential, as creativity, empathy, and strategy are uniquely human skills that cannot be replicated by machines. We are at a critical time where we can create a world that is smarter, more efficient, and more human.

Key Takeaways

1. Prioritize diversity and inclusion in the development of AI and robotics to mitigate bias and reinforce social equality.
2. Develop a culture that embraces the use of AI and automation while also valuing human skills, creativity, and emotional intelligence.
3. Take advantage of the rapidly developing technology of human augmentation, which can enhance human abilities beyond what is naturally possible.
4. Use human augmentation technologies such as bionics, cybernetics, exoskeletons, and gene editing to provide advantages in areas such as job performance, athletics, and medical rehabilitation.
5. Use transhuman technologies to help individuals with disabilities or injuries to regain their independence and improve their quality of life, and to provide new opportunities for medical professionals to diagnose and treat illnesses.
6. View automation and AI as partners, not replacements for humans, and focus on the potential benefits of these technologies to unlock new levels of innovation and productivity.
7. Provide education and training programs for employees to acquire the skills and knowledge required for new job roles created by the integration of advanced technologies.
8. Foster a culture of continuous learning and development in the workplace.
9. Empower diverse teams with a range of skills and perspectives to work independently and make decisions based on the best interests of the business.

10. Provide mental health resources and support systems for individuals and teams impacted by the integration of AI and technology.
11. Prioritize education and training to prepare for the future of work, with employers providing opportunities for lifelong learning and reskilling.
12. Address ethical concerns related to human augmentation, such as discrimination, inequality, and potential risks to health and safety, by basing decisions on merit rather than physical enhancements that may not be accessible to all.
13. Develop clear ethical and legal frameworks to guide the development and use of AI and robotics.
14. Create clear guidelines and policies for the ethical use of AI in the recruitment process to avoid discrimination.
15. Ensure that automation and AI work in tandem with humans, creating a balanced system that benefits everyone.

Glossary

1. *Algorithmic Bias:* Systematic and repeatable errors in a computer system that create unfair outcomes, such as privileging one arbitrary group of users over others.

2. *Artificial General Intelligence (AGI):* AI systems with general cognitive abilities such that they can outperform humans at most economically valuable work.

3. *Augmented Reality (AR):* A technology that superimposes a computer-generated image on a user's view of the real world, providing a composite view.

4. *Autoencoders:* A type of artificial neural network used for learning efficient codings of input data.

5. *Autonomous Robots:* Robots that can perform desired tasks in unstructured environments without continuous human guidance.

6. *Big Data:* Refers to extremely large data sets that may be analyzed computationally to reveal patterns, trends, and associations.

7. *Brain-Computer Interface (BCI):* A collaboration between a brain and a device that enables signals from the brain to direct some external activity, such as control of a cursor or a prosthetic limb.

8. *Biohacking:* The practice of changing our bodies and our brains at the most fundamental level with the aim of moving beyond what's currently possible for human beings.

9. *Cobots:* A robot designed to work in conjunction with humans in a shared workspace. They are usually designed to be safe and, in contrast to traditional industrial robots, can interact with human coworkers.

10. *Cognitive Enhancement:* Improvements in the cognitive function of individuals, through either pharmacological or non-pharmacological means, such as brain stimulation or nootropic drugs.

11. *Computer Vision:* A field of AI that trains computers to interpret and understand the visual world.

12. *Cybernetic Enhancement:* The use of technology to enhance the capabilities of the human body beyond its natural limits.

13. *Data Cleaning/Wrangling:* The process of correcting and consolidating raw data to prepare it for analysis.

14. *Data Mining:* The process of discovering patterns in large data sets involving methods at the intersection of machine learning, statistics, and database systems.

15. *Deep Learning:* A subset of machine learning that's based on artificial neural networks with representation learning.

16. *Digital Divide:* The gap between demographics and regions that have access to modern information and communications technology, and those that don't or have restricted access.

17. *End of Arm Tooling (EOAT):* The device at the end of a robotic arm designed to interact with the environment. The exact nature of this device depends on the required task.

18. *Exoskeletons:* Wearable devices that work in tandem with the user. They can be made to assist with increased strength and endurance.

19. *Explainability/Interpretability:* The extent to which a machine learning model's behavior can be understood.

20. *Generative Adversarial Networks (GANs):* A class of AI algorithms used in unsupervised machine learning, implemented by a system of two neural networks contesting with each other in a zero-sum game framework.

21. *Genetic Enhancement:* The use of genetic engineering to increase the baseline capabilities of an individual, such as strength, agility, or cognitive function.

22. *Gig Economy:* A labor market characterized by the prevalence of short-term contracts or freelance work as opposed to permanent jobs.

23. *Labeled data:* A group of samples that have been tagged with one or more labels. Labeling typically takes raw input data and adds informational tags to that data based on what is being observed. These labels can be for a single class or multiple classes.

24. *Lifelong Learning:* The "ongoing, voluntary, and self-motivated" pursuit of knowledge for either personal or professional reasons.

25. *Mixed Reality (MR):* A blend of physical and digital worlds, unlocking the links between human, computer, and environment interaction.

26. *Myoelectric Prosthetics:* Prosthetics that use the electrical signals generated by the user's remaining muscles to control the device.

27. *Neuroprosthetics:* A series of devices that can substitute a motor, sensory, or cognitive modality that might have been damaged as a result of an injury or a disease.

28. *Natural Language Processing (NLP):* A subfield of AI that focuses on the interaction between computers and humans through natural language.

29. *Neural Network:* A computational model used in machine learning which is designed to simulate the behavior of human neurons in the brain.

30. *Osseointegration:* A surgical procedure that allows direct skeletal attachment of prosthetic limbs. The procedure involves implanting a metal rod into the bone, which then protrudes through the skin to attach to a prosthesis.

31. *Overfitting:* When a machine learning model learns the training data too well, it may perform poorly on unseen data because it has also learned the noise in the training data.

32. *Physical Enhancement:* Any modification of the human body aimed at improving performance, appearance, or capability.

33. *Privacy Concerns:* Issues or concerns about the collection, use, disclosure, and storage of personal data by organizations.

34. *Prompt engineering:* Atechnique used in natural language processing, and particularly with transformer-based models like GPT-3 and GPT-4. The idea is to carefully craft the input prompt to the model in order to guide it toward producing a specific kind of output.

35. *Prosthesis:* An artificial device that replaces a missing body part, which may be lost through trauma, disease, or a condition present at birth.

36. *Reinforcement Learning:* An approach in machine learning where an agent learns to make decisions by performing actions in an environment to maximize some notion of cumulative reward.

37. *Remote Work:* A flexible working style that allows professionals to work outside of a traditional office environment.

38. *Reskilling:* The process of learning new skills so you can do a different job, or training people to do a different job.

39. *Retraining:* The process of teaching new skills or training in a new technique or technology to the existing workforce.

40. *Robot Manipulator:* An arm-like mechanical device often used in manufacturing or assembly.

41. *Robotics Process Automation (RPA):* The use of software with AI and machine learning capabilities to handle high-volume, repeatable tasks.

42. *Robot Programming:* The process of providing a robot with instructions on how to complete tasks. With cobots, this often includes teaching by demonstration where a human operator guides the robot through a task manually.

43. *Supervised Learning:* An approach in machine learning where the model is provided with labeled training data.

44. *Transformer Models:* A type of model in natural language processing, particularly in the field of transformers, such as the GPT family.

45. *Upskilling:* The process of teaching existing employees new skills to utilize within their current roles.

46. *Unsupervised Learning:* An approach in machine learning where the model is provided with unlabeled training data and asked to find patterns or relationships.

47. *Virtual Reality (VR):* A simulated experience that can be similar to or completely different from the real world.

48. *Workforce Automation:* The application of technology to automate tasks previously performed by humans.

Epilogue: The Ghost Writers

In the Machine

In early 2017, I set out to write this book, with a draft outline on my laptop and ideas parading around in my head. It wasn't until I found like-minded people at an AI company that I realized I had been going about it the wrong way. I needed a co-author, someone to help me get past occasional blocks and bounce ideas off, but not a full ghostwriter - more of a ghostwriter in the machine. That's when I realized my idea was right: "there is AI in team." My writing team could be a partnership between me and AI.

Some readers may be skeptical of this approach, concerned about the reliability of information or the validity of the writing. But as with any ghostwriter partnership or writer/editor relationship, there is a measured amount of give-and-take to achieve a great narrative and factual accounting. Several team members, including another human who performed the final editing and proofreading from a "human point of view," contributed to the process. Whether the partner is human or machine is to some degree irrelevant, as long as it is indeed a partnership.

To be fully transparent about the process, I will share with you how we wrote this book. Wherever AI played its part, a human could have done the work as well. The difference is that the AI is available whenever and wherever I need it. It is incredibly fast at creating multiple variations of ideas based on my notes and research, and, except for a tendency to use passive voice, is incredibly accurate in terms of grammar and punctuation. The key to getting it to work was to go back to 2010, when I made a presentation on the future of education, training, and learning. Threaded throughout the presentation was a theme I would come back to as recently as this year. The theme is that fundamental change is necessary for humans to advance to the next stage of development. We

206

must teach children and adults not just the basics of reading, writing, and arithmetic, but also how to ask the right questions and effectively explain what we want as results. Ironically, whether collaborating with a machine or another human being, this skill is vital and currently lacking in many of us. As of this year, this is now known as "prompt engineering."

So, here is the process we (me and AI) used (see the prompts used to generate portions of the chapter rough drafts in the Appendix):

1. Ken develops several Alexa skills.
2. Ken presents his methodology for a new type of interactivity for game development and training tools at various conferences.
3. Participants at the conferences suggest that Ken write a book on the topic.
4. Ken conducts research on the subject and drafts an outline for the book.
5. Ken writes an abstract for each chapter but experiences writer's block for a year.
6. Ken revisits the book and updates it with new information because the field is constantly evolving.
7. Ken discovers GPT-3 and uses it to expand his abstracts by inputting the abstract and asking the AI to identify key takeaways and ask questions for more information.
8. AI lists a set of key takeaways.
9. Ken uses his personal research and Google to find additional supporting materials and data for each topic or subtopic.
10. Ken uses the new body of information to expand the abstracts into rough chapters.
11. Ken prompts the AI to use the chapter as a starting point and determine key subtopics, then research and produce a new version of the chapter approximately 4000 words long.
12. AI produces the new chapters with mixed results.
13. Ken reviews the chapters, expands on ideas or removes irrelevant content, and ensures that important content hasn't been removed by the AI.

14. Ken has the AI analyze his writing samples to determine his writing style.
15. Ken prompts the AI to apply his writing style to each chapter for consistent tone and flow.
16. AI rewrites each chapter with mixed results. It sometimes takes a couple of tries to get it close enough to be worth editing.
17. Ken performs a "final" edit.
18. Ken uses a grammar and plagiarism checker to proofread each chapter and fix any narrative or plagiarism issues.
19. Ken prompts the AI to generate stories as examples to provide context for each chapter.
20. Ken selects the best versions for the book and performs a final edit for each.
21. Ken asks the AI to generate a list of Action Items for each chapter of the book.
22. AI creates the list of action items for each chapter.
23. Ken has several humans review the book to ensure the writing does not sound too artificial, and to validate citations.
24. Reviewer's feedback results in a total re-scaffolding of the book including removing some chapters and adding a new ending.
25. Ken collects the stories up front as a full preface.
26. Ken performs additional research to support some of the chapters with additional data and industry references to validate his conclusions.
27. Industry experts and scholars review and help shape the final book.
28. Ken has an editor do a final proofread and edit.
29. Ken performs his own final, final edit of the entire book.
30. The cover artist creates the cover.
31. Ken creates the chapter art.

As we head into this new age of content creation, you can either embrace these new tools and electronic partners or you can hide from them. By leveraging this technology, I have augmented my own creativity with the speed of execution only possible by AI. Those who adopt them will be able to create amazing things in time frames that are almost too short to believe. While the ideation for this book took several years, the execution to finish it took less than four months. The rest was just a matter of self-publishing and promoting the title.

My hope with this book is to remove fear and empower you and your team to embrace the diversity that comes from everyone participating together: humans, cyborgs, and cobots. "There is AI in Team" is more than just a catchy phrase. It's a call to action. We must embrace AI as a partner, not a replacement, and work together to build a brighter future.

Appendix

Prompt Engineering for this Book

Prompt engineering is the process of designing and optimizing prompts for natural language processing (NLP) models. Prompts are the initial text or questions that are presented to an NLP model to generate a response. The goal of prompt engineering is to create prompts that are effective in eliciting the desired response from the model. This involves selecting the right words and phrases, structuring the prompt in a way that is easy for the model to understand, and testing and refining the prompts to improve their performance. Prompt engineering is an important part of building high-performing NLP models, as the quality of the prompts can have a significant impact on the accuracy and effectiveness of the model. In practice, the prompt helps adjust the model weights to complete a specific task, but it's more of an art than a science.

Prompt engineering is similar to how a business professional might prepare clear guidelines for a project or a proposal. By carefully crafting these prompts, you ensure that the AI understands your requirements and provides relevant, accurate, and valuable responses, ultimately enhancing the efficiency and effectiveness of your business interactions with the AI system. This means that the user interacts with the AI model by typing or speaking a prompt that is then converted to text from which the model responds with predictions of written text based on the training data stored in the large language model (LLM). It often requires experience, intuition, and experimentation to create a prompt that yields a successful outcome.

Here is a list of the prompts I used in creating the early drafts of this book by inserting my notes and ideas and then asking the AI to help me develop the body of the text. From these drafts, I then expanded the chapters, edited and restructured them, added more content and supporting data, and ultimately finished the book.

I used Chat GPT and Soffos Chat generative AI writing as draft scaffolding, and in some cases draft content. Using this base, I conducted additional research and wrote a significant amount of original material in addition to editing and rewriting the content generated by AI. One particular note to consider when using generative AI, is that it tends to be redundant, writes in passive voice, and does not cite references (and in some cases makes stuff up). It also caps out at 4000 characters or so, which does not by any means constitute a complete chapter.

Here is the list of Chat GPT and Soffos Chat prompts:

1. Use the following research materials and preliminary book outline and create a logical set of chapters with the target audience set to the average employee ages 18 to 65 at a high school education level.
2. Expand each chapter to include a set of topics and subtopics from which I can perform additional research.
3. Provide a brief introduction for each chapter.
4. Determine the key topics and subtopics of the following chapter and discuss and expand each by applying additional research "Enhancing Human Capabilities Beyond Biology…"
5. Write a story of life in the day of a modern video producer who uses generative artificial intelligence to enhance his operational efficiency and allow him to focus on his creative ideas. He uses AI to help him write scripts, create shot lists, search for locations, generate animation, create voice over audio and music, and to work with him to produce incredible videos in a fraction of the time previously required.

Start the story at an action point and fill in the details of what happened earlier in the production as the story proceeds.

6. Write a story about a salesperson who uses augmented reality glasses with image recognition software to help him identify and remember objects, locations, and people to enhance his sales capability by supplementing his knowledge with information AI can go out and find for him. This same AI uses natural language processing to analyze his conversations and behaviors to provide audio feedback on his performance and recommend actions for improvement. All the while the visual display of the glasses provides additional information from his email and calendar to allow him to be more productive during his day. Start the story as he is heading into a sales meeting and add details of how he prepared for the day and how the day ends as the story progresses.

7. Determine the key topics and subtopics of the following chapter and discuss and expand each by applying additional research "The $6 Billion Dollar Person: Exploring the Landscape of Human Augmentation..."

8. Write a scenario depicting the average day of an employee who has had augmentations performed on their bodies that enhance their appearance and increase their capabilities beyond their normal human peers. start the story in the middle of morning where the employee is in the midst of doing a task as a part of a larger team effort. During the scenario, introduce what happened as he prepared for work and what will happen after the team effort is complete. Write the story with more emphasis on how he accomplishes a set of tasks as a part of a diverse team and how their jobs are impacted by his capabilities. Reduce the use of terminology specific to human augmentation. Use this chapter as some background information to provide context for human augmentation.

9. Write a story from the perspective of a human resources talent recruiter who is hiring a candidate for a service technician position that requires excellent memory recall of repair procedures and strength to lift heavy parts and equipment. The recruiter is comparing two individuals, each who have several years of experience,

214

however, one of them has physical augmentations that make them more capable than a normal human and the other is normal. What are the ethical considerations the recruiter must make in order to comply with rules of inclusion and diversity and equity as it relates to each job applicant. Use the following chapter to support your story

10. Determine the key topics and subtopics of the following chapter and discuss and expand each by applying additional research "Human, Transhuman, Non-Human..."

11. Write a human-interest story where humans, augmented humans, and non-humans or cobots must work together at a company whose human resource department is not prepared to manage the new requirements for recruiting, developing, and training these teams to be effective. Use the following chapter for context.

12. Write a human interest story where humans, augmented humans, and non-humans or cobots must work together at a company whose human resource department is dealing with a situation where one of the human employees has filed a discrimination lawsuit against the company because her inclusive and diverse team of humans, augmented humans, and non-humans or cobots have placed her in a role she feels is too dangerous for her and she cannot equally compete for other opportunities. Use the following chapter for context.

13. Determine the key topics and subtopics of the following chapter and discuss and expand each by applying additional research: "There is AI in TEAM..."

14. Provide more examples and expand this chapter by applying additional research and discussing each of the topics and subtopics in more detail: "Levelling the Playing Field..."

15. Expand this chapter by incorporating additional research from online sources and discussing each of the topics and subtopics in more detail: "Levelling the Playing Field..."

16. Rewrite and expand this chapter to 4000 words by performing additional online research and discussing each of the topics and subtopics in more detail "Adoption vs. Adaptation..."

17. Expand on the topic of corporate and individual employee Adaptation vs. Adoption in the context of the chapter you just wrote.

18. List the key takeaways in this chapter: "Adoption vs. Adaptation..."

19. Write a human-interest story about two employees in the age of AI and human augmentation, one that adapts to the changes and one who adopts the new age and embraces the opportunity. Focus on the feelings of the characters in the story and how their lives are impacted. Use the following chapter for context: "Adoption vs. Adaptation..."

20. Write a third person perspective human interest story about three employees in the age of AI and human augmentation, one that adapts to the changes and one who adopts the new age and embraces the opportunity, and the third was their manager who was responsible for effective change management. Focus on the feelings of the characters in the story and how their lives are impacted. Use the following chapter for context: "Adoption vs. Adaptation..."

21. Rewrite and add content to this chapter by incorporating additional research you conduct online and discussing each of the chapter topics and subtopics in more detail: "The 3 Laws of Robotics..."

22. Write a human-interest story about what happens when an Artificial Intelligence becomes a member of the board of directors for a pharmaceutical corporation and the company must make decisions based on what is described in the following chapter for context: "The 3 Laws of Robotics..."

23. List the key takeaways in the following: "The Three Laws of Robotics..."

24. Write a human-interest story for People Magazine about the human factor in the age of AI and human augmentation. Focus on the feelings of the characters in the story. Use the following chapter for context: "The Human Factor..."

25. Write a human-interest story for Scientific American about the human factor in the age of AI and human augmentation. Focus on the data behind why humans are the untold secret to the success of AI and robotics. Use the following chapter for context: "The Human Factor..."

26. Write a human-interest story for Training Magazine about the human factor in the age of AI and human augmentation. Focus on the data behind why a partnership between humans and machines is critical for meeting the needs of elementary education. Use the following chapter for context: "The Human Factor..."
27. List the key takeaways in the following: "The Human Factor..."
28. List the key takeaways in the following "Synthetic Fear..."
29. Write a topic section on "Fear of AI and robotics is not entirely irrational, but much of it is based on myths, misconceptions, and pop culture references."
30. Write a topic section on "AI and robotics are designed to augment human capabilities, not replace them."
31. Write a topic section on "Education and awareness can help dispel myths and reduce fear and promote a more accurate understanding of AI and robotics."
32. Write a topic section on "Ethical and legal frameworks are needed to guide the development and use of AI and robotics and reduce fear in the general human population."
33. Write a topic section on "Public awareness campaigns can help demystify AI and robotics and address common misconceptions."
34. List the key takeaways in the following: "Mental Health in the Age of AI..."
35. Write a topic section on "The integration of AI in our daily lives has brought about a host of benefits, including increased efficiency, accuracy, and convenience. However, there are concerns about the potential impact on mental health, both for humans and for our machine counterparts."
36. Write a chapter outline on "The primary concerns regarding metal health as a result of the influx of AI, robotics and human augmentation include the loss of purpose that can come with the increased automation of certain jobs and tasks and the increasing dependence on technology and the internet."
37. Write a topic section on "The COVID-19 pandemic has exacerbated the issues related to AI, virtual connections, remote devices, and technology dependency."

217

38. Write a topic section on "We need to prioritize social relationships and find ways to foster connections even in a world that is increasingly digital and automated, and we must continue to invest in mental health resources and support systems."

39. Write a medical journal article covering the state of mental health in the age of AI, natural language processing, augmentation, and automation using this information and anything you can find as a reference "Mental Health in the Age of AI..."

40. Write a fictional case study on employee mental health for Web MD using the online references and the following information "Chapter 10: Mental Health in the Age of AI..."

41. Write a fictional case study on industrial manufacturing employee mental health for Web MD using the online references and the following information "Mental Health in the Age of AI..."

42. Write a fictional article on junior high school student mental health for and Educational Journal using the online references and the following information "Mental Health in the Age of AI..."

43. Write a fictional blog from a junior high school student facing mental health challenges related to ChatGPT for learning and the following information "Mental Health in the Age of AI..."

44. List the key takeaways in the following "More Than a Numbers Game..."

45. Write a topic section on "There is a high level of uncertainty in the current employment landscape, with many employees concerned about job displacement due to automation and AI."

46. Write a topic section on "To prepare for the future of work, it is important to prioritize education and training, with employers providing opportunities for lifelong learning and reskilling and educational institutions adapting to the changing needs of the labor market."

47. Write a topic section on "Vocational education is an important part of preparing students and employees for jobs in the 21st century, but there are challenges to achieving consistency and effectiveness in a global skills market."

48. Write a topic section on "How technology can help workers in the gig economy demonstrate their skills and qualifications to potential employers."

49. Write a story for Money Magazine about a female corporate executive who went back to vocational school to learn to program in order to build a side hustle creating mobile apps. Use the following for reference "summarize "More Than a Numbers Game…"

50. Write a story about an assembly line worker who was worried about being replaced by a robot and so started a side hustle creating online how-to videos and made it a career. Use the following for reference "More Than a Numbers Game…"

51. List the key takeaways in the following: "AI Should be Blind…"

52. Write an outline on "Inclusivity in the workplace is crucial as the world becomes more diverse. Transhumanism presents both opportunities and challenges for businesses."

53. Write an outline on "HR practices must evolve to identify worker skills and competencies and remove bias from recruitment algorithms."

54. Write an article for HR Today about how the use of AI in HR business practices should be without bias. Use the following for reference: "AI Should be Blind…"

55. Write a story for HR Today about how the use of AI in HR business practices can impact potential employees and should be without bias. Use the following for reference: "AI Should be Blind…"

56. Write a first-person story for HR Today about how the use of AI in HR business practices impacted you, a potential employee, and should have been without bias. Use the following for reference: "AI Should be Blind…"

57. Write a 3rd person story for HR Today about how the use of AI in HR business practices impacted Mary, a potential employee, and should have been without bias. Use the following for reference: "AI Should be Blind…"

58. List the key takeaways in the following: "The Zero-Sum Game…"

59. Write an outline on "Automation and AI have the potential to unlock new levels of innovation and productivity that were previously unattainable."

60. Write an outline on "Machines should be viewed as partners, not as replacements for humans."

61. Write an outline on "The concept of a zero-sum game is a fallacy that fails to account for the interconnectedness and interdependence of humanity and technology."

62. Write a story about how the application of AI, automation, human augmentation, and robots is improving the odds of the average person around the globe as relates to the zero-sum game referred to in the following "The emergence of transhumanism and technological advancements...

Citations

1. "AI Ethics." IBM, https://www.ibm.com/topics/ai-ethics.
2. "AI-Powered Drones Revolutionize Wildlife Conservation." IO, 5 Mar. 2023, innovationorigins.com/en/laio/ai-powered-drones-revolutionize-wildlife-conservation/.
3. "David W Sime - Lenovo Future of You Interview." YouTube, 30 Mar. 2022, www.youtube.com/watch?v=Vd96hxDlbqg&t=194s.
4. "Dealing with Employees Who Resist Technological Change." Innovu, https://www.innovu.com/post/dealing-with-employees-who-resist-technological-change.
5. "Explainable AI (XAI)." IBM, https://www.ibm.com/watson/explainable-ai.
6. "5 Ways Automation Will Change the Business Landscape." Business Class: Trends and Insights | American Express, www.americanexpress.com/en-us/business/trends-and-insights/articles/5-ways-automation-will-change-the-business-landscape?linknav=en-US-oneAmex-axpSearchResults-7&searchresult=Artificial%2BIntelligence. Accessed 10 May 2023.
7. "Ford Rolls Out Exoskeleton Wearable Technology Globally To Help Lessen Worker Fatigue, Injury." Ford Media Center. media.ford.com/content/fordmedia/fna/us/en/news/2018/08/07/ford-rolls-out-exoskeleton-wearable-technology-globally-to-help-.html. Accessed 10 May 2023.
8. "Generative Design at Airbus: Customer Stories." *Autodesk*, www.autodesk.com/customer-stories/airbus. Accessed 10 May 2023.
9. "How IOT and AI Solutions Can Accelerate EV Deployments and Enhance Customer Experience." NASSCOM Community | The Official Community of Indian IT Industry, https://community.nasscom.in/index.php/communities/emerging-tech/how-iot-and-ai-solutions-can-accelerate-ev-deployments-and-enhance.
10. "How Will Ai Change the World?" TED, www.ted.com/talks/ted_ed_how_will_ai_change_the_world/c/transcript?language=en. Accessed 17 May 2023.
11. "Learn & Earn: Track Cryptocurrency Prices & Learn Crypto!" BitDegree.org Crypto Learning Hub, https://www.bitdegree.org/.
12. "National Center for Manufacturing Education (NCME)." ATE Central, https://atecentral.net/r7727/national_center_for_manufacturing_education_ncme.
13. "Our Programs." Amazon Safety US, safety.aboutamazon.com/our-programs. Accessed 20 May 2023.

14. "Principles and Practices for Building More Trustworthy AI." IBM Newsroom, newsroom.ibm.com/Principles-and-Practices-for-Building-More-Trustworthy-AI. Accessed 20 May 2023.

15. "Reimagining Energy: News and Insights: Home." Bp Global, www.bp.com/en/global/corporate/news-and-insights/bp-magazine/cool-technology-transforming-safety.html. Accessed 20 May 2023.

16. "Sanctuary AI Unveils PhoenixTM - A Humanoid General-McKinsey Technology Trends Outlook 2022. McKinsey & Company, Aug. 2022, https://www.mckinsey.com/~/media/McKinsey/Business%20Functions/McKinsey%20Digit al/Our%20Insights/The%20top%20trends%20in%20tech%20final/Tech-Trends-Exec-Summary.

17. "Sustainable Development." EUR, https://eur-lex.europa.eu/EN/legal-content/glossary/sustainable-development.html#:~:text=Sustainable%20development%20was%20defined%20in,to%20m eet%20their%20own%20needs'.

18. "The Impact of Artificial Intelligence on the Future of Workforces." https://www.whitehouse.gov/wp-content/uploads/2022/12/TTC-EC-CEA-AI-Report-12052022-1.pdf.

19. "Unlock Your Company's Knowledge." Sana Labs, 2023, https://www.sanalabs.com/.

20. "Virtual Business Meeting of the CDC/HRSA Advisory Committee on HIV, Viral Hepatitis, and STD Prevention and Treatment." Centers for Disease Control, US Department of Health and Human Services Centers for Disease Control and Prevention Health Resources and Services Administration, 20 Apr. 2021, https://www.cdc.gov/faca/committees/pdfs/chachspt/chachspt-minutes-20210420-21-508.pdf.

21. "What Are Robotic Teach Pendants?" Robots Done Right - Used Robot Sales, robotsdoneright.com/Articles/what-are-robotic-teach-pendants.html. Accessed 7 June 2023.

22. "Will Artificial Intelligence Create Useless Class of People?" Performance by Yuval Noah Harari, YouTube, YouTube, 28 Oct. 2021, https://www.youtube.com/watch?v=7FzNUc-ZFv4. Accessed 7 Mar. 2023.

23. Admin, Web. "Exploring the World of Deep Learning: CNNS, RNNS, and Gans."
     Exploring the World of Deep Learning: CNNs, RNNs, and GANs, Blogger, 22 Jan. 2023,
     https://neuralyzed.blogspot.com/2023/01/exploring-world-of-deep-learning-cnns.html.

24. Andreason, Stuart, et al. "The Digital Divide and the Pandemic: Working from Home and
     Broadband and Internet Access." Federal Reserve Bank of Atlanta, 29 June 2020,
     https://www.atlantafed.org/cweo/workforce-currents/2020/06/29/the-digital-divide-and-the-
     pandemic-working-from-home-and-broadband-and-internet-access.aspx.

25. Artificial Intelligence and Ethics: An Emerging Area of Board Oversight Responsibility.
     Posted by Vivek Katyal, Cory Liepold, and Satish Iyengar, Deloitte & Touche LLP, on
     Thursday, June 25, 2020 (Vivek Katyal is Chief Operating Officer, Risk and Financial
     Advisory, and Cory Liepold and Satish Iyengar are Principals, Risk and Financial Advisory,
     at Deloitte & Touche LLP. This post is based on a Deloitte memorandum by Mr. Katyal,
     Mr. Cory Liepold, Mr. Iyengar, Nitin Mittal, and Irfan Saif.)

26. Asimov, Isaac. "Runaround." Runaround. Rutgers University, n.d. Web. 28 Apr. 2014.

27. Atske, Sara. "3. Improvements Ahead: How Humans and Ai Might Evolve Together in the
     next Decade." Pew Research Center: Internet, Science & Tech, Pew Research Center, 15
     Sept. 2022, https://www.pewresearch.org/internet/2018/12/10/improvements-ahead-how-
     humans-and-ai-might-evolve-together-in-the-next-decade/.

28. Baylor University. "People afraid of robots are much more likely to fear losing their jobs
     and suffer anxiety-related mental health issues, study finds." ScienceDaily. ScienceDaily, 21
     March 2017. http://www.sciencedaily.com/releases/2017/03/170321125007.htm.

29. Beer, Patrick, and Regina H. Mulder. "The Effects of Technological Developments on Work
     and Their Implications for Continuous Vocational Education and Training: A Systematic
     Review." Frontiers, Frontiers, 14 Apr. 2020,
     https://www.frontiersin.org/articles/10.3389/fpsyg.2020.00918/full.

30. Ben Dickson, et al. "There's a Huge Difference between AI and Human Intelligence-so
     Let's Stop Comparing Them." TechTalks, 14 Oct. 2018,
     https://bdtechtalks.com/2018/08/21/artificial-intelligence-vs-human-mind-brain.

31. Betancourt, Alejandro. "Transhumanism: The Transformation of the Human Race. Should It
     Matter to You?" Medium, ILLUMINATION, 14 Nov. 2021,
     https://medium.com/illumination/transhumanism-the-transformation-of-the-human-race-
     should-it-matter-to-you-1adfd426a34e.

32. Boutin, Chad. "There's More to AI Bias than Biased Data, NIST Report Highlights." NIST, 16 Mar. 2022, https://www.nist.gov/news-events/news/2022/03/theres-more-ai-bias-biased-data-nist-report-highlights.

33. Building the Bionic Brain - Falksangdata.no. https://falksangdata.no/wp-content/uploads/2021/05/TechRepublicBionicBrainEbook.pdf.

34. Candelon, François, et al. "Synthetic Biology Is about to Disrupt Your Industry." BCG Global, BCG Global, 4 Oct. 2022, https://www.bcg.com/publications/2022/synthetic-biology-is-about-to-disrupt-your-industry.

35. Cheng, Wayne. "Amper Music Custom Composition: Blog: Ai Lyrics, Song, and Music Tool." Audoir, LLC, 30 Apr. 2021, https://www.audoir.com/ampermusic.

36. Chui, Michael, et al. "The State of AI in 2022-and a Half Decade in Review." McKinsey & Company, McKinsey & Company, 6 Dec. 2022, https://www.mckinsey.com/capabilities/quantumblack/our-insights/the-state-of-ai-in-2022-and-a-half-decade-in-review.

37. Clark, Donald. "PedAIgogy – New Era of Knowledge and Learning Where Ai Changes Everything." PedAIgogy – New Era of Knowledge and Learning Where AI Changes Everything, 2 Mar. 2023, https://donaldclarkplanb.blogspot.com/2023/03/pedaigogy-new-era-of-knowledge-and.html.

38. Constantz, Jo. "Ai Tools Bring Low Skilled Workers Big Productivity Boost, Study Reveals." Bloomberg.Com, 24 Apr. 2023, www.bloomberg.com/news/articles/2023-04-24/generative-ai-boosts-worker-productivity-14-new-study-finds.

39. Cox, Alistair. "'the Great Resignation': Why Are so Many Thinking about Quitting?" Viewpoint - Careers Advice Blog, 2 Aug. 2021, https://social.hays.com/2021/08/02/the-great-resignation-why-so-many-people-quitting/).

40. Cross, Rob. "To Be Happier at Work, Invest More in Your Relationships." Harvard Business Review, 10 Sept. 2019, https://hbr.org/2019/07/to-be-happier-at-work-invest-more-in-your-relationships.

41. Daniel, Robin R. "Artificial Intelligence and Its Impact on Future Jobs." Education, Jan. 2023, https://vocal.media/education/artificial-intelligence-and-its-impact-on-future-jobs.

42. Diamandis, Peter H. "Why AI Is Exploding Now!" Peter Diamandis - Innovation & Entrepreneurship Community, Peter H. Diamandis, 23 Apr. 2023, https://www.diamandis.com/blog/ai-exploding-now?hss_channel=lis-kQX_GK_W7C.

43. Dick, Ellysse. "The Promise of Immersive Learning: Augmented and Virtual Reality's Potential in Education." ITIF, 30 Aug. 2021, https://itif.org/publications/2021/08/30/promise-immersive-learning-augmented-and-virtual-reality-potential/.

44. Dilmegani, Cem. "What Is Human Augmentation? (with Examples and Technologies)." AIMultiple, 23 Jan. 2023, https://research.aimultiple.com/human-augmentation/.

45. Dredge, Stuart. "Musk: 'You Can't Have a Person Driving a Two-Ton Death Machine'." Business Insider, Business Insider, Mar. 2015, https://www.businessinsider.com/musk-you-cant-have-a-person-driving-a-two-ton-death-machine-2015-3.

46. Dua, André, et al. "Freelance, Side Hustles, and Gigs: Many More Americans Have Become Independent Workers." McKinsey & Company, McKinsey & Company, 23 Aug. 2022, https://www.mckinsey.com/featured-insights/sustainable-inclusive-growth/future-of-america/freelance-side-hustles-and-gigs-many-more-americans-have-become-independent-workers.

47. Eskills Malta Foundation Digital Skills National Survey Results. Jan. 2022, https://eskillsalliancecms.gov.mt/en/nationalsurveyresults/Documents/PWC_Survey%20report_final_.pdf.

48. Forum, World Economic. "Don't Fear Ai. It Will Lead to Long-Term Job Growth." Forbes, Forbes Magazine, 26 Oct. 2020, https://www.forbes.com/sites/worldeconomicforum/2020/10/26/dont-fear-ai-it-will-lead-to-long-term-job-growth/.

49. Gallagher, James. "New Superbug-Killing Antibiotic Discovered Using AI." BBC News, 25 May 2023, www.bbc.com/news/health-65709834.

50. Gillespie, Patrick. "Intuit: Gig Economy Is 34% of US Workforce." CNNMoney, Cable News Network, 24 May 2017, https://money.cnn.com/2017/05/24/news/economy/gig-economy-intuit/index.html.

51. Gleeson, Brent. "8 Steps for Helping Your Employees Accept Change." Forbes, Forbes Magazine, 12 Oct. 2022, https://www.forbes.com/sites/brentgleeson/2016/10/17/8-steps-for-helping-your-employees-accept-change/?sh=747d200a29f2.

52. Griffin, De'Onn, and Mark Coleman. "Gartner." 27 Feb. 2018.

53. Harwell, Drew. "Tech's Hottest New Job: Ai Whisperer. No Coding Required." The Washington Post, WP Company, 27 Feb. 2023,

226

https://www.washingtonpost.com/technology/2023/02/25/prompt-engineers-techs-next-big-job/.

54.	Haswell, Holli. "Under Armour and IBM to Transform Personal Health and Fitness, Powered by IBM Watson." Phys.Org, 2016, phys.org/news/2016-01-armour-ibm-personal-health-powered.html.

55.	Healion, Chloe. "The Benefits of Collaborative Robotics for Safety and Productivity in Manufacturing." Safety Indicators, 3 Mar. 2023, https://www.safetyindicators.com/general/collaborative-robotics-for-safety-and-productivity-in-manufacturing/.

56.	Herper, Matthew. "Here's Why We're Not Prepared for the next Wave of Biotech Innovation." STAT, 3 Nov. 2022, https://www.statnews.com/2022/11/03/why-were-not-prepared-for-next-wave-of-biotech-innovation/.

57.	"Introducing… Khanmigo! – Khan Academy Help Center." Khan Academy, 2023, https://support.khanacademy.org/hc/en-us/community/posts/13992414612877-Introducing-Khanmigo-.

58.	Kande, Mohamed. "Don't Fear Ai. the Tech Will Lead to Long-Term Job Growth." World Economic Forum, 6 Oct. 2020, https://www.weforum.org/agenda/2020/10/dont-fear-ai-it-will-lead-to-long-term-job-growth/.

59.	Kevin Reilly, Charlie Wood. "Quantum Computing, Climate Change, and Interdependent Ai: Academics and Execs Predict How Tech Will Revolutionize the next Decade." Business Insider, Business Insider, https://www.businessinsider.com/davos-microsoft-tech-henry-blodget-panel-2020-1?r=US&IR=T&_lrsc=e936f4c9-a8b5-48fd-9f82-a16e0db7b587.

60.	Khan, Sal. "Sal Khan: How Ai Could Save (Not Destroy) Education." *Sal Khan: How AI Could Save (Not Destroy) Education | TED Talk*, www.ted.com/talks/sal_khan_how_ai_could_save_not_destroy_education/c/transcript. Accessed 17 May 2023.

61.	Kite-Powell, Jennifer. "Collaborative Robots Make a Comeback in 2021." Forbes, 20 Apr. 2022, www.forbes.com/sites/jenniferhicks/2022/04/19/collaborate-robots-make-a-comeback-in-2021/.

62. Kolisis, Nikolaos, and Fragiskos Kolisis. "Synthetic Biology: Old and New Dilemmas-the Case of Artificial Life." MDPI, Multidisciplinary Digital Publishing Institute, 20 July 2021, https://www.mdpi.com/2673-6284/10/3/16.

63. Langman S, Capicotto N, Maddahi Y, Zareinia K. Roboethics principles and policies in Europe and North America. SN Appl Sci. 2021;3(12):857. doi: 10.1007/s42452-021-04853-5. Epub 2021 Nov 7. PMID: 34790889; PMCID: PMC8572833.

64. Leibowitz, David. "'sherlock Holmes' Ai Diagnoses Disease Better than Your Doctor, Study Finds." Medium, 15 Oct. 2020, towardsdatascience.com/ai-diagnoses-disease-better-than-your-doctor-study-finds-a5cc0ffbf32.

65. Lee, Nicol Turner, et al. "Algorithmic Bias Detection and Mitigation: Best Practices and Policies to Reduce Consumer Harms." Brookings, Brookings, 9 Mar. 2022, https://www.brookings.edu/research/algorithmic-bias-detection-and-mitigation-best-practices-and-policies-to-reduce-consumer-harms/.

66. Leech, Nancy L, et al. "The Challenges of Remote K–12 Education during the COVID-19 Pandemic: Differences by Grade Level." Online Learning, vol. 26, no. 1, 2022, https://doi.org/10.24059/olj.v26i1.2609.

67. Liepold, Cory, et al. "Artificial Intelligence and Ethics: An Emerging Area of Board Oversight Responsibility." The Harvard Law School Forum on Corporate Governance, 25 June 2020, https://corpgov.law.harvard.edu/2020/06/25/artificial-intelligence-and-ethics-an-emerging-area-of-board-oversight-responsibility/.

68. Lombardo, Kevin. "A Proactive Approach to Musculoskeletal Health Through Ergonomics." DORN, 15 Aug. 2018, https://www.dorncompanies.com/a-proactive-approach-to-musculoskeletal-health-through-ergonomics/.

69. Lutino, Cielo. "How Does Technology Impact Politics?" Acquia, 18 Aug. 2022, https://www.acquia.com/blog/how-does-technology-impact-politics.

70. Magnuson, Markus Amalthea. "What Is Transhumanism?" What Is Transhumanism?, https://whatistranshumanism.org/.

71. Manyika, James, et al. "Jobs Lost, Jobs Gained: What the Future of Work Will Mean for Jobs, Skills, and Wages." McKinsey & Company, McKinsey & Company, 28 Nov. 2017, https://www.mckinsey.com/featured-insights/future-of-work/jobs-lost-jobs-gained-what-the-future-of-work-will-mean-for-jobs-skills-and-wages.

72. Marche , Stephen. "The Apocalypse Isn't Coming. We Must Resist Cynicism and Fear about Ai." The Guardian, 15 May 2023, www.theguardian.com/commentisfree/2023/may/15/artificial-intelligence-cynicism-technology.

73. Markets, Research and. "Global Human Augmentation Market to Reach \$341.2 Billion by 2026 at a 21% CAGR." PR Newswire: Press Release Distribution, Targeting, Monitoring and Marketing, 12 Sept. 2022, https://www.prnewswire.com/news-releases/global-human-augmentation-market-to-reach-341-2-billion-by-2026-at-a-21-cagr-301621916.html.

74. Marlar, Jenny. "Assessing the Impact of New Technologies on the Labor Market: Key Constructs, Gaps, and Data Collection Strategies for the Bureau of Labor Statistics." U.S. Bureau of Labor Statistics, Gallup, 7 Feb. 2020, https://www.bls.gov/bls/congressional-reports/assessing-the-impact-of-new-technologies-on-the-labor-market.htm.

75. Martinez, Carole. "Artificial Intelligence Enhances Accessibility for People with Disabilities." Inclusive City Maker, 24 Jan. 2022, https://www.inclusivecitymaker.com/artificial-intelligence-accessibility-examples-technology-serves-people-disabilities/.

76. Maslej, Nestor, and Shana Lynch. "AI Index 2023." Stanford Institute for Human-Centered Artificial Intelligence, 3 Apr. 2023, https://hai.stanford.edu/research/ai-index-2023.

77. Milligan, Susan. "HR 2025: 7 Critical Strategies to Prepare for the Future of HR." SHRM, SHRM, 16 Aug. 2019, https://www.shrm.org/hr-today/news/hr-magazine/1118/pages/7-critical-strategies-to-prepare-for-the-future-of-hr.aspx.

78. Mohammed Eslami, Aaron Adler. "Artificial Intelligence for Synthetic Biology." ACM, 1 May 2022, https://cacm.acm.org/magazines/2022/5/260341-artificial-intelligence-for-synthetic-biology/fulltext.

79. Murdoch, Nicole. "Nicole Murdoch on Linkedin: #Cybersecurity #Ai #Innovation #Respect #Work: 82 Comments." Nicole Murdoch on LinkedIn: #Cybersecurity #Ai #Innovation #Respect #Work | 82 Comments, LinkedIn, 21 Apr. 2023, https://www.linkedin.com/feed/update/urn:li:activity:7055047205870587905/.

80. Nast, Condé, director. President Barack Obama on How Artificial Intelligence Will Affect Jobs. Wired, Conde Nast, 10 Dec. 2016, https://www.wired.com/video/watch/president-barack-obama-on-how-artificial-intelligence-will-affect-jobs. Accessed 9 Mar. 2023.

81. Neubauer, Aljoscha C. "The Future of Intelligence Research in the Coming Age of Artificial Intelligence – with a Special Consideration of the Philosophical Movements of Trans- and Posthumanism." Intelligence, vol. 87, 2021, p. 101563., https://doi.org/10.1016/j.intell.2021.101563.

82. Newsroom. "Top 10 Emerging Technologies to Watch in 2020." Modern Diplomacy, 16 Nov. 2020, https://moderndiplomacy.eu/2020/11/17/top-10-emerging-technologies-to-watch-in-2020/.

83. Newsroom. "Top 10 Emerging Technologies to Watch in 2020." Modern Diplomacy, 16 Nov. 2020, https://moderndiplomacy.eu/2020/11/17/top-10-emerging-technologies-to-watch-in-2020/.

84. Nikumbh, Tejas. "Artificial Intelligence (AI): Introduction, Application & Goals " Tejas Nikumbh." Tejas Nikumbh, 3 Feb. 2023, https://tejasnikumbh.com/artificial-intelligence-ai/.

85. O'Leary, John, et al. "Future-Proofing the Labor Force." Deloitte Insights, Deloitte, 1 Apr. 2022, https://www2.deloitte.com/us/en/insights/industry/public-sector/government-trends/2022/future-government-workforce-development.html.

86. Ormandy, Elisabeth H, et al. "Genetic Engineering of Animals: Ethical Issues, Including Welfare Concerns." The Canadian Veterinary Journal = La Revue Veterinaire Canadienne, U.S. National Library of Medicine, May 2011, https://www.ncbi.nlm.nih.gov/pmc/articles/PMC3078015/.

87. Palena Neale, Ph.D. "Council Post: Leveling up: The Benefits of Upskilling for Employees and Organizations." Forbes, Forbes Magazine, 8 Nov. 2022, https://www.forbes.com/sites/forbescoachescouncil/2022/05/23/leveling-up-the-benefits-of-upskilling-for-employees-and-organizations/?sh=355dbb3045a5.

88. Paneque-Gálvez, Jaime, et al. "Grassroots Innovation Using Drones for Indigenous Mapping and Monitoring." MDPI, 7 Dec. 2017, doi.org/10.3390/land6040086.

89. Paris, Francesca, and Larry Buchanan. "35 Ways Real People Are Using A.I. Right Now." The New York Times, The New York Times, 14 Apr. 2023, https://www.nytimes.com/interactive/2023/04/14/upshot/up-ai-uses.html.

90. "Pause Giant AI Experiments: An Open Letter." Future of Life Institute, 21 Apr. 2023, https://futureoflife.org/open-letter/pause-giant-ai-experiments/.

91. Petrin, Martin. "Corporate Management in the Age of AI." Columbia Business Law Review, vol. 2019, no. 3, 1 Dec. 2019, https://doi.org/https://doi.org/10.7916/d8-0kt5-dc36.

92. Pietrykowski, Bruce, and Michael Folster. "Boundary Crossings: Collaborative Robots and Human Workers." AnthroSource, 2019, anthrosource.onlinelibrary.wiley.com/doi/full/10.1111/1559-8918.2019.01290.

93. Poll, Sylvia. "'New Technologies Have Made Sport More Inclusive.'" Peace and Sport I Be Part of What Matters, 22 July 2019, https://www.peace-sport.org/opinion/new-technologies-have-made-sport-more-inclusive/.

94. President, Julia Cusick Vice, et al. "Preparing American Students for the Workforce of the Future." Center for American Progress, 29 Oct. 2021, https://www.americanprogress.org/article/preparing-american-students-workforce-future/.

95. Press, The Associated. "U.S. Warns of Discrimination in Using Artificial Intelligence to Screen Job Candidates." NPR, NPR, 12 May 2022, https://www.npr.org/2022/05/12/1098601458/artificial-intelligence-job-discrimination-disabilities.

96. Rainie, Lee. "The Future of Jobs and Jobs Training." Pew Research Center: Internet, Science & Tech, Pew Research Center, 15 Sept. 2022, https://www.pewresearch.org/internet/2017/05/03/the-future-of-jobs-and-jobs-training/.

97. Rajbhandari, Abhishek. "Week 10." Herald, 2 Feb. 2023, https://aeysama.wordpress.com/week-10/.

98. Rawal, Yogesh. "5 Reasons Why Adopting New Technology Is Important for Any Business." Medium, Akeo, 24 Aug. 2021, https://medium.com/akeo-tech/5-reasons-why-adopting-new-technology-is-important-for-any-business-b0ac113d4019.

99. Reed, Eric. "What Is a Zero Sum Game and Why Is It Important in 2019? - Thestreet." The Street, The Street, 26 Dec. 2018, https://www.thestreet.com/politics/what-is-a-zero-sum-game-14818535.

100. Rheinland, TÜV. "New Normal Solutions." New Normal Solutions | TÜV Rheinland, https://www.tuv.com/landingpage/en/new-normal-solutions/.

101. Romero, Enzo. "Enzo Romero: The Affordable, 3D-Printed Bionics of the Future." Enzo Romero: The Affordable, 3D-Printed Bionics of the Future | TED Talk, www.ted.com/talks/enzo_romero_the_affordable_3d_printed_bionics_of_the_future/transcript. Accessed 17 May 2023.

102. Schork, Nicholas J. "Artificial Intelligence and Personalized Medicine." Cancer Treatment and Research, U.S. National Library of Medicine, 2019, https://www.ncbi.nlm.nih.gov/pmc/articles/PMC7580505/.

103. Sciences, Contributor(s): National Academies of. "Information Technology and the U.S. Workforce: Where Are We and Where Do We Go from Here?" Where Are We and Where Do We Go from Here? |The National Academies Press, 16 Mar. 2017, https://doi.org/10.17226/24649.

104. Silver, Mike. "Scientists Create the next Generation of Living Robots." Tufts Now, 31 Mar. 2021, https://now.tufts.edu/2021/03/31/scientists-create-next-generation-living-robots.

105. Skates, Anne Lee. "Five Predictions for the Future of Learning in the Age of AI." Andreessen Horowitz, 8 Feb. 2023, https://a16z.com/2023/02/08/the-future-of-learning-education-knowledge-in-the-age-of-ai/.

106. SR2020. "Robo-Banking: Artificial Intelligence at JPMorgan Chase." Digital Innovation and Transformation, d3.harvard.edu/platform-digit/submission/robo-banking-artificial-intelligence-at-jpmorgan-chase/. Accessed 20 May 2023.

107. Statt, Nick. "Amazon Says Fully Automated Shipping Warehouses Are at Least a Decade Away." The Verge, 1 May 2019, www.theverge.com/2019/5/1/18526092/amazon-warehouse-robotics-automation-ai-10-years-away.

108. Stevens, Richard W. "Panic Propaganda Pushes Surrender to Ai-Enhanced Power." Mind Matters, 9 May 2023, mindmatters.ai/2023/05/panic-propaganda-pushes-surrender-to-ai-enhanced-power/.

109. Tristianto, Bimo Putro. "Ai and Emotion: Can We Teach Machines to Feel?" Medium, MLearning.ai, 18 Dec. 2022, https://medium.com/mlearning-ai/ai-and-emotion-can-we-teach-machines-to-feel-83f4d4b53030.

110. Turner, Jordan. "6 Ways the Workplace Will Change in the next 10 Years." Gartner, 6 July 2022, https://www.gartner.com/smarterwithgartner/6-ways-the-workplace-will-change-in-the-next-10-years.

111. Villasenor, John. "How CHATGPT Can Improve Education, Not Threaten It." Scientific American, Scientific American, 10 Feb. 2023, https://www.scientificamerican.com/article/how-chatgpt-can-improve-education-not-threaten-it/.

112. Vincent, James. "Robots and Ai Are Going to Make Social Inequality Even Worse, Says New Report." The Verge, The Verge, 13 July 2017, https://www.theverge.com/2017/7/13/15963710/robots-ai-inequality-social-mobility-study.

113. Webber, Sheila & Detjen, Jodi & Maclean, Tammy & Thomas, Dominic. (2019). Team challenges: Is artificial intelligence the solution?. Business Horizons. 62. 10.1016/j.bushor.2019.07.007.

114. Whang, Oliver. "'Consciousness' in Robots Was Once Taboo. Now It's the Last Word." The New York Times, The New York Times, 6 Jan. 2023, https://www.nytimes.com/2023/01/06/science/robots-artificial-intelligence-consciousness.html.

115. "Why People and Ai Make Good Business Partners | Shervin Khodabandeh | Ted." YouTube, 22 May 2022, www.youtube.com/watch?v=1yQYySYN2io.

116. Willmer, Gareth. "Helping the Body and Brain to Welcome Bionic Limbs and Implants." Horizon Magazine, 12 Oct. 2022, https://ec.europa.eu/research-and-innovation/en/horizon-magazine/helping-body-and-brain-welcome-bionic-limbs-and-implants.

117. Zahidi, Saadia. "We Need a Global Reskilling Revolution – Here's Why." World Economic Forum, https://www.weforum.org/agenda/2020/01/reskilling-revolution-jobs-future-skills/.

About the Author

Ken Hubbell is a pragmatic futurist whose philosophy is "design for tomorrow, build for today." He started his career creating interactive videos and animation, and later moved into designing and programming serious games and simulations. He is a leader in learning and development, AI, and other innovative technologies. He enjoys the challenge of growing and leading talented individuals, bringing them together to design and build engaging products.

Through the years he has worked with some incredible people and amazing organizations including the United Nations, Caterpillar, NASA, the FAA, and WUNC-TV to name a few. He is known for aligning diverse team members and functional units, drawing on their experiences, and building award winning games, applications, and educational technology. Ken is a firm believer in changing the dynamics of traditional human resources to meet the needs of our growing transhumanist workforce.

Ken received his Bachelor of Industrial Product Design degree from North Carolina State University and his Master of Science in Instructional Technology degree from East Carolina University. He is currently Chief Product Officer for Soffos Inc., a low-code natural language processing and generative AI platform. He is a passionate coach, mentor, writer, and international speaker who enjoys sharing his experiences and giving back to others.